REEF FISHES
& CORALS
EAST COAST OF SOUTHERN AFRICA

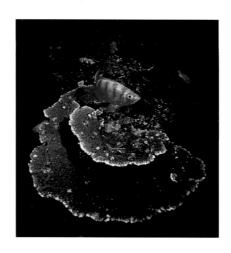

REEF FISHES

& CORALS

EAST COAST OF SOUTHERN AFRICA

DENNIS KING

ACKNOWLEDGEMENTS

From the inception of this book five years ago to its completion, a number of people, including close friends, have assisted me with various aspects of its development. However, I would first like to thank my long-suffering dive buddies for bearing with me – sometimes in difficult circumstances. It is always a problem when you want to stay longer in one spot to get those special photographs, while the rest of the dive group wants to move on!

I would like to mention the following authorities who gave their time and expertise to confirm identifications and to comment on the text. Dr Phil Heemstra (fish), Simon Chater (fish), Dr P. Ramsay (corals), Bernhard Riegl (corals), Michael Schleyer (corals) and Judy Mann (text). I would also like to thank Alex Azzopardi and Kim Fong for assisting with the initial layout of the book and cover design for submission to potential publishers prior to acceptance of the book by the Struik Group. My thanks also goes to Shelly Brummer and Barbara Weston for assisting with the illustrations, and to Alan Mountain for his encouragement and advice. A special thanks must go to Sherilee Nairn who has uncomplainingly typed numerous versions of the text over the five years. Also to my wife and family for their support during the many hours I spent in writing the text.

Finally, I would like to express my appreciation to Pippa Parker and Maggie Mouton, who have done a wonderful job in editing the text, and to the designer, Mandy Moss, and the rest of the Struik team involved in the book.

DENNIS KING
(DURBAN 1996)

PHOTOGRAPHIC NOTES

All the photographs in this book were taken by the author over a period of 15 years. The photographs were taken using a Nikon F single lens reflex camera with an action view finder housed in an Ikelite housing, together with a Sunpack Marine 32 flash unit. Small species were taken with a 105 mm macro lens and the larger species with a 55 mm macro lens. A few photographs were taken with a 28 mm lens. Fujichrome 100 ASA film was used almost exclusively.

Struik Publishers
(a division of New Holland Publishing (South Africa) (Pty) Ltd)
80 McKenzie Street
Cape Town 8001

First published: 1996
8 10 9

New Holland Publishing is a member of Johnnic Communications Ltd.
Visit us at **www.struik.co.za**

www.imagesofafrica.co.za
IMAGES OF AFRICA
PHOTO LIBRARY

Front cover (clockwise): Coral rockcod, Yellowtail rockcod, Powder blue surgeon, Group of reef fishes; *Inset:* Thistle coral; *P 1:* Crescent-tail bigeye and plate coral, Sodwana Bay; *pp 2–3:* Thistle soft coral and goldies, Seven-Mile Reef, Sodwana Bay; *p. 5:* Tiger angelfish; *p. 7:* Potato bass and bluestreak cleaner wrasse; *p 9:* Seafans and bluebanded snappers; *p 10:* Reef scene at Two-Mile Reef, Sodwana Bay; *pp 102–103:* Reef scene at Seven-Mile Reef, Sodwana Bay; *p 104:* 'Fleshy soft coral'

ISBN 1 86825 981 1

CONTENTS

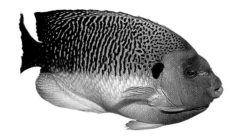

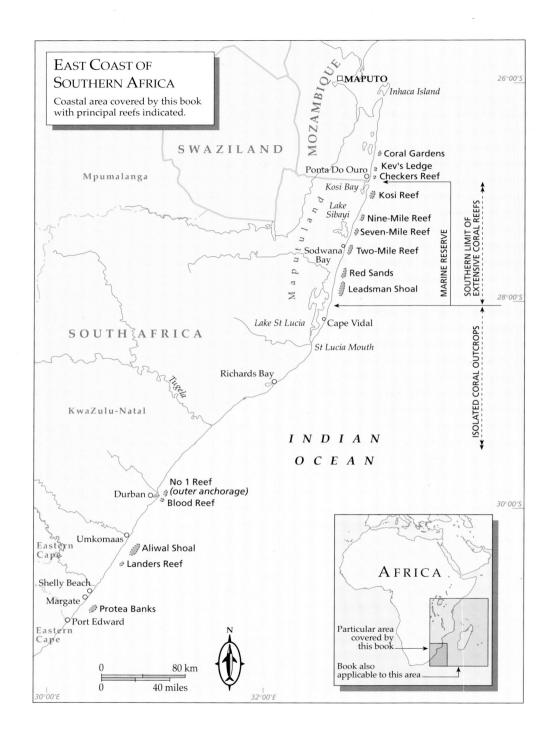

East Coast of Southern Africa

Coastal area covered by this book with principal reefs indicated.

MOZAMBIQUE

□ **MAPUTO**

Inhaca Island

26°00'S

SWAZILAND

Mpumalanga

Coral Gardens
Ponta Do Ouro
Kev's Ledge
Checkers Reef

Kosi Bay
Kosi Reef

Lake Sibayi
Nine-Mile Reef
Seven-Mile Reef

Sodwana Bay
Two-Mile Reef

Red Sands
Leadsman Shoal

MARINE RESERVE

SOUTHERN LIMIT OF EXTENSIVE CORAL REEFS

28°00'S

Lake St Lucia
Cape Vidal

St Lucia Mouth

SOUTH AFRICA

ISOLATED CORAL OUTCROPS

Tugela

Richards Bay

KwaZulu-Natal

I N D I A N

O C E A N

No 1 Reef
(outer anchorage)
Durban
Blood Reef

30°00'S

Eastern Cape
Umkomaas
Aliwal Shoal
Landers Reef

Shelly Beach
Margate
Protea Banks
Port Edward

Eastern Cape

N

| 0 | | 80 km |

| 0 | | 40 miles |

30°00'E

32°00'E

AFRICA

Particular area covered by this book

Book also applicable to this area

GENERAL INTRODUCTION

The aim of this book is to provide scuba divers and snorkellers with a compact, basic guide to the identification of the more common reef fishes and corals found in the area from Protea Banks off the coast of southern KwaZulu-Natal to Inhaca Island off the coast of southern Mozambique (see map opposite). The emphasis on fishes and corals is because they represent the most prominent animals observed by divers on most tropical and subtropical reefs. As corals are often neglected in books of this nature, it was considered necessary to include such an identification guide to introduce under-water enthusiasts to the fascinating but complex world of corals.

This book is not intended in any way to be a scientific work and, as such, details regarding the structure of fish, the numbers of fin rays, etc. are not given, and only limited information on coral biology and taxonomy is provided. The terminology is also kept simple. Readers who wish to pursue their investigations further may consult the more detailed works listed under the Suggested Further Reading section on page 121.

Many of the fish and coral species described here have a much wider distribution and occur throughout the western Indian Ocean, including areas such as East Africa, the Seychelles, the Comoros, Mauritius and Madagascar. Some species even occur further afield in the Indian Ocean and the western Pacific Ocean. Visitors to these regions will also find this book useful.

Each species entry provides brief details on the descriptive features of the fish or coral, as well as its habitat and diet. Clear, full-colour photographs are featured for each fish and coral, which are essential for identification.

The maximum recorded size attained for each fish species is included, but, since most individual fish never reach this size, the diver will generally see smaller specimens than those indicated here. Larger individuals of some species tend to occur at greater depths, beyond the reach of most sport divers.

The colours of some fishes present a problem because, not only can certain fishes change colour according to mood and background, but also the colours and shapes of juveniles can be very different from those of the adults. The depth of water influences colour; the red end of the spectrum filters out as the depth increases. Note that all the photographs used in this book have been taken using a flash, therefore the true colours are shown and not necessarily those seen underwater. Where a description in the text notes, 'varies from reddish-brown to olive-brown or grey', it means that the fish could be any of these colours or shades in between.

The local distribution of fish species and corals has generally been limited to stating whether they occur on coral reefs (from Maputaland north-wards), or on rocky reefs (south of Maputaland) (see map opposite), or on both. Certain fish species included are endemic to the East Coast and rarely, if at all, occur north of Maputaland. The depth range of fishes and corals may well be found to be shallower or deeper than stated.

For each fish species the common English and Afrikaans names are provided, following *Smith's Sea Fishes* (Southern Book Publishers, 1988). Where relevant, alternative English names are also given in parenthesis. The scientific name of each fish species is provided, and species are grouped into families – some families comprising many species, others just a single species. Because of the lack of local knowledge regarding coral identification, the species name is not always given. In instances where there is doubt, only the genus is provided. Further, many corals do not have recognised common names either, and in such instances new names have been suggested. Alternative common names are given in parenthesis.

Much has yet to be learned about the mysteries of the reef – a natural history that only began to unfold with the advent of scuba. Even today, divers are still pioneers. After studying this book for just a few hours, readers will be amazed at how quickly they will learn to recognise the fishes and corals included here. And after only a few dives your personal count will grow to 20 or 50 or more. But the fun begins when an unfamiliar species is sighted. You will become an underwater detective, looking for clues that might reveal the identity of the 'mystery' fish or coral. What is required is alertness, stalking skills (in the case of fishes), attention to detail, and memory. For fish, the size, body shape, fin arrangement, colour markings and habitat must be recorded. In the case of corals, the form or shape, colour, texture and habitat are keys to identification.

When diving, remember to abide by the rules for safe diving and to avoid touching the reef. As a diver, be part of the preservation of the underwater environment and help to prevent it from being spoiled by human thoughtlessness, ignorance and greed.

HOW TO USE THIS BOOK

FISH SECTION

The ease with which species are identified with the aid of this book depends very much on what is known about fishes to start with. Having some idea of what the most common and numerous fishes of a particular family look like would make identification much easier. Thus, when there is a spare moment, study the various families and, in particular, common fishes such as butterflyfishes, angelfishes, damsels and wrasses.

To assist with the identification process, line-drawings of the fish families are displayed on pages 12–15. These have been grouped together according to similar characteristics, such as 'silvery in colour' or 'odd-shaped swimmers'. To identify a fish, first decide to which group it belongs, then look for the family by studying the line-drawings. A page reference refers the reader to photographs of individual species for further identification. Details of each family are given in the text opposite, together with the physical characteristics, distinguishing features, habitat and diet of the individual species. When identifying fishes, try to memorise certain features such as overall shape, colour, patterns and position of spots or lines. Other features may also help, such as the presence of one or two dorsal fins, a round or V-shaped tail, etc. Remember also that the colour of a fish changes with depth.

CORAL SECTION

Before attempting to identify corals it is necessary to understand the different characteristics of the main coral types, that is, hard coral, soft coral, etc. given on pages 104–107. This prior knowledge will greatly assist the diver in identifying the coral type. The next stage would be to identify the coral genus by studying features such as overall shape, variations in growth form, structure and arrangement of corallites, colour and habitat from the photographs of and text on the individual corals.

It must be remembered that the identification of corals is a difficult task due to the similarity of many corals and the variations in growth form that can occur within a particular coral genus. Therefore, a good understanding of the subject is essential for accurate identification.

ABBREVIATIONS
mm = millimetre; cm = centimetre; m = metre; sp = species; p. = page

FISHES

INTRODUCTION

CARTILAGINOUS FISHES

Cartilaginous fishes include sharks, rays, skates and guitarfishes. Although they are similar to bony fishes in general design and anatomy, they have a number of distinguishing characteristics, the most significant being the structure of the skeleton which, unlike that of bony fishes, is composed of cartilage and not true bone. The five to seven gill slits of cartilaginous fishes are not protected by a covering and are exposed. Both jaws have rows of teeth which are continually replaced throughout the life of the animal. The fins of cartilaginous fishes also differ from those of bony fishes as they are fleshy, spineless and more ridged. Tough teeth-like projections cover the skin of most sharks and give it a sandpaper-like surface.

All cartilaginous fishes are carnivorous. Reproduction in these fishes is characterised by internal fertilisation, which is followed by one of three developmental patterns. Some sharks lay eggs (catsharks); others give birth to live young (Zambezi shark); while yet others retain the developing embryos in the oviducts (or uterus) until the young are born alive (raggies). About 350 different species of cartilaginous fishes have been identified worldwide.

BONY FISHES

Bony fishes have a true bone skeleton and flexible fins supported by bony spines and soft rays. A single gill cover on either side of the head protects the gill chamber, housing the respiratory gill arches and filaments. The majority of bony fishes are covered with a protective layer of scales, although a few families – such as barbels (seacatfishes) and eels – are scaleless.

External fertilisation is common in marine bony fishes, with large numbers of eggs and sperm being released into the water in close proximity. Some fishes, such as damselfishes, lay their eggs on the substratum, where they are fertilized directly. An important feature in the reproduction of bony fishes is the ability of some species to change their sex. Certain fishes are born female but change sex to male when they attain a particular size. Other species change from male to female, while others can reverse their sex when required. This process helps to ensure the maximum reproductive potential of the particular species. Bony fishes form the largest and most diverse group of vertebrate animals on earth. Some 22 000 species have been recorded in all aquatic habitats.

EXTERNAL FEATURES OF FISHES

The external features of cartilaginous and bony fishes referred to in the identification process are indicated in the diagrams below.

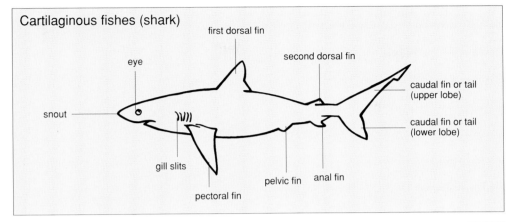

Cartilaginous fishes (shark)

first dorsal fin

second dorsal fin

eye

caudal fin or tail (upper lobe)

snout

caudal fin or tail (lower lobe)

gill slits

pelvic fin   anal fin

pectoral fin

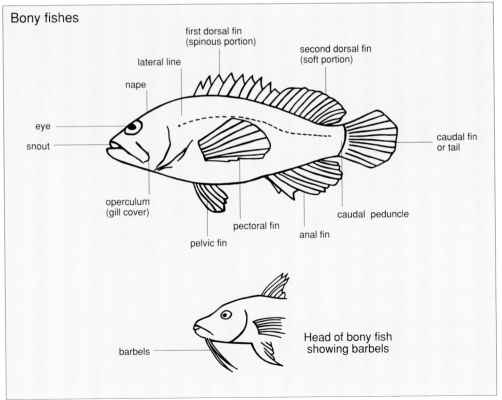

Bony fishes

first dorsal fin (spinous portion)

second dorsal fin (soft portion)

lateral line

nape

eye

snout

caudal fin or tail

operculum (gill cover)

caudal peduncle

pectoral fin

anal fin

pelvic fin

barbels

Head of bony fish showing barbels

IDENTIFICATION GROUPS AND PICTORIAL GUIDE TO FAMILIES

The following illustrations are line-drawings of the fish families contained in this book. Families sharing a common characteristic are grouped together for initial identification.

Sharks and rays

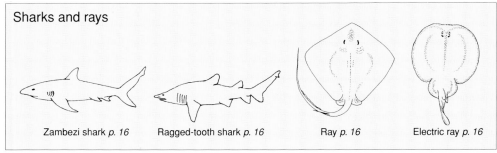

Zambezi shark *p. 16*   Ragged-tooth shark *p. 16*   Ray *p. 16*   Electric ray *p. 16*

Odd-shaped swimmers

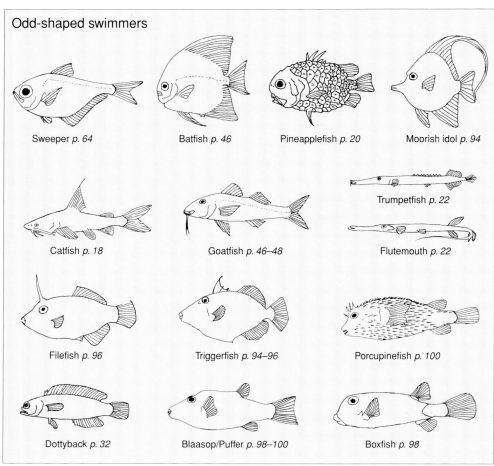

Sweeper *p. 64*   Batfish *p. 46*   Pineapplefish *p. 20*   Moorish idol *p. 94*

Catfish *p. 18*   Goatfish *p. 46–48*   Trumpetfish *p. 22*

Flutemouth *p. 22*

Filefish *p. 96*   Triggerfish *p. 94–96*   Porcupinefish *p. 100*

Dottyback *p. 32*   Blaasop/Puffer *p. 98–100*   Boxfish *p. 98*

Odd-shaped/Bottom-dwellers

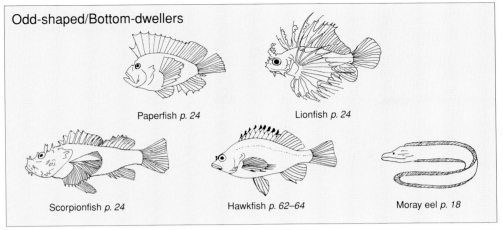

Paperfish *p. 24*

Lionfish *p. 24*

Scorpionfish *p. 24*

Hawkfish *p. 62–64*

Moray eel *p. 18*

Silvery in colour

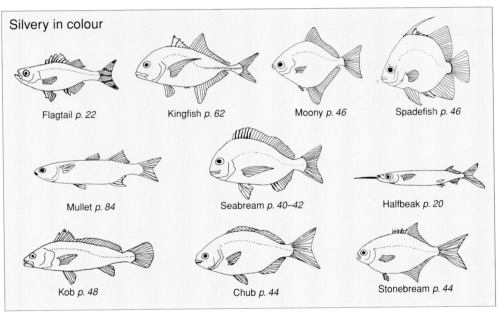

Flagtail *p. 22*

Kingfish *p. 62*

Moony *p. 46*

Spadefish *p. 46*

Mullet *p. 84*

Seabream *p. 40–42*

Halfbeak *p. 20*

Kob *p. 48*

Chub *p. 44*

Stonebream *p. 44*

Sloping head/Tapered body

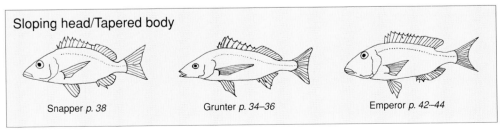

Snapper *p. 38*

Grunter *p. 34–36*

Emperor *p. 42–44*

Disc or oval-shaped/Colourful

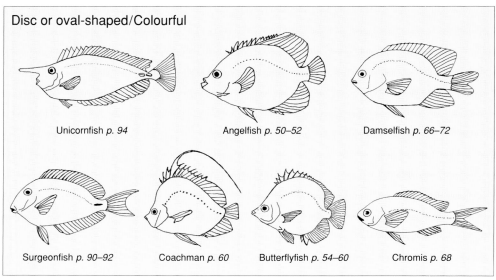

Unicornfish *p. 94*   Angelfish *p. 50–52*   Damselfish *p. 66–72*

Surgeonfish *p. 90–92*   Coachman *p. 60*   Butterflyfish *p. 54–60*   Chromis *p. 68*

Heavy body/Large lips

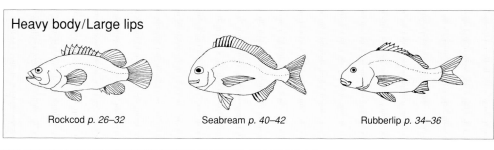

Rockcod *p. 26–32*   Seabream *p. 40–42*   Rubberlip *p. 34–36*

Big eyes/Cave-dwellers

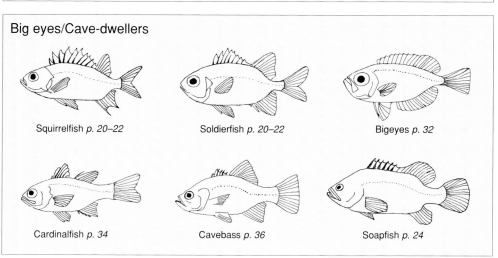

Squirrelfish *p. 20–22*   Soldierfish *p. 20–22*   Bigeyes *p. 32*

Cardinalfish *p. 34*   Cavebass *p. 36*   Soapfish *p. 24*

Regular-shaped swimmers

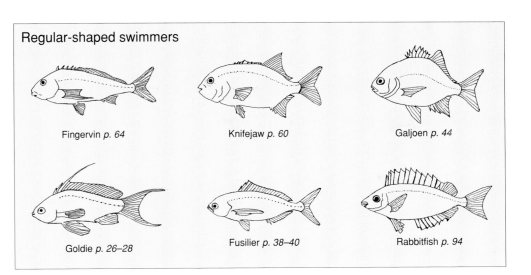

Fingervin *p. 64*

Knifejaw *p. 60*

Galjoen *p. 44*

Goldie *p. 26–28*

Fusilier *p. 38–40*

Rabbitfish *p. 94*

Swim with pectoral fins

Parrotfish *p. 82–84*

Wrasse *p. 72–82*

Hogfish/Wrasse *p. 72–74*

Small elongated bottom-dwellers

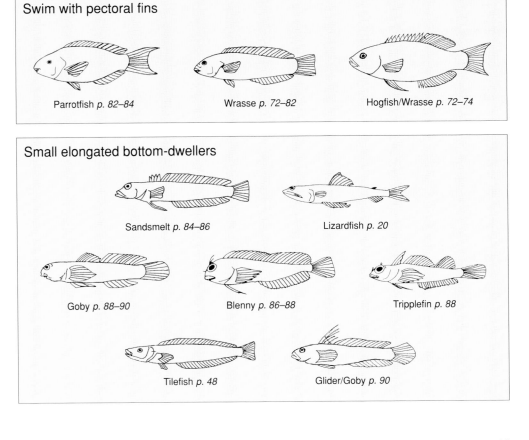

Sandsmelt *p. 84–86*

Lizardfish *p. 20*

Goby *p. 88–90*

Blenny *p. 86–88*

Tripplefin *p. 88*

Tilefish *p. 48*

Glider/Goby *p. 90*

SHARKS

Sharks have cartilaginous skeletons and sandpaper-like skins covered with tiny teeth-like projections instead of scales. They also have five to seven gill slits on either side of the head, and fleshy fins. Adult males have paired claspers used during mating. Most sharks are solitary, but some congregate during their mating season. The majority are harmless, but some are potentially dangerous to man.

Requiem Sharks – Family Carcharhinidae

Zambezi shark (Bull shark) *Carcharhinus leucas*

Attains 300 cm. A potentially dangerous shark, predominantly grey with a pale underside, a rounded, blunt snout and sharp, serrated, triangular teeth. Has a worldwide distribution in warmer seas; inhabits coastal waters, estuaries and rivers. Preys on bony fish, small sharks, dolphins and turtles.

Ragged-tooth Sharks – Family Odontaspididae

Spotted ragged-tooth shark ('Raggie') *Eugomphodus taurus*

Attains 300 cm. Has a robust, pale brown body with a coppery sheen and sparsely spaced dark brown spots, a pointed snout, small eyes and slender, pointed teeth, raggedly arranged in rows. Dangerous only when provoked. Common on coral and rocky reefs, preferring shallow water. During their annual migration northwards from the Eastern Cape, congregations of pregnant raggies are found at specific reefs along the KwaZulu-Natal coast. Preys on fish, small sharks and crustaceans.

RAYS

Rays have cartilaginous skeletons, flattened bodies and greatly expanded pectoral fins fused to the head, giving them a disc-like shape. Below the pectoral fins are five to six gill slits. Many have a whip-like tail armed with one or two sharp spines which are used for defence. Rays are not aggressive and retaliate only if provoked. Sandsharks appear more shark-like than ray-like and have a flat body with expanded pectoral fins and a well-developed tail. Most rays and sandsharks live close to sandy bottoms.

Guitarfishes or Sandsharks – Family Rhinobatidae

Greyspot guitarfish (Greyspot sandshark) *Rhinobatos leucospilus*

Attains 92 cm. Has a sand-brown body, blue-grey and brown spots and a pale underside. This common fish lives on sandy bottoms inshore to depths of 40 m. Feeds on small fish, crabs and molluscs.

Electric Rays – Family Torpedinidae

Marbled electric ray *Torpedo sinuspersici*

Attains a disc width of 90 cm. Has a fleshy body and short, stocky tail. Mottled brown overall with many irregular lighter blotches. Produces an electric shock to stun prey. Common along sandy shores and reefs. Buries itself in sand with only its eyes visible. Feeds on slow-swimming fish and molluscs.

Stingrays – Family Dasyatidae

Bluespotted ribbontail ray *Taeniura lymma*

Attains a disc width of 75 cm. Has bright blue spots on a yellowish-brown body. Common on rocky and coral reefs and rocky shores. Partly buries itself in sand. Feeds on crabs, worms and shrimps.

Round ribbontail ray (Giant reef ray) *Taeniura melanospilos*

Attains a disc width of 160 cm. A large ray with a round body, grey to dark grey on top with a pattern of variable-sized black spots, and a white underside. Widespread; inhabits shallow and deep coral and rocky reefs. Often buries itself in sand. Feeds mainly on shrimps and molluscs.

Zambezi shark

Spotted ragged-tooth shark

Greyspot guitarfish

Marbled electric ray

Bluespotted ribbontail ray

Round ribbontail ray

Moray Eels – Family Muraenidae

Moray eels are slender, snake-like fish which lack scales and pelvic and pectoral fins. They constantly open and close their large mouths to move water over their gills for respiration, and have sharp fang-like teeth. Although not aggressive towards divers, they can inflict a nasty bite if provoked. Most are secretive during the day and hide in recesses in the reef, but are occasionally seen with their heads protruding from their shelters. They are voracious nocturnal hunters of small fish and octopus, and detect their food by smell.

Honeycomb moray *Gymnothorax favagineus*

Attains 200 cm. One of the largest and most conspicuous moray eels. It has a distinctive dark brown to black body with a yellowish-white honeycomb pattern. Inhabits coral and rocky reefs that range in depth from 10-30 m. This common moray eel is inquisitive when encountered by divers, but can be unpredictable and should not be fed as it can inflict a serious bite when annoyed. Feeds on fish and octopus, the latter being particularly favoured.

Blackcheek moray (Masked moray) *Gymnothorax breedeni*

Attains 65 cm. Has a distinctive black mark behind the eye, extending to the corner of the mouth; body is brown with darker speckles. Not a common moray, it occurs on both rocky and coral reefs ranging from the Aliwal Shoal area northwards. Found in depths of 10-30 m. Feeds mainly on fish. By day it often extends its head from a crevice or hole.

Guineafowl moray *Gymnothorax meleagris*

Attains 80 cm. Relatively uncommon, this rather shy eel is recognised by the numerous small white spots on a dark brown body and by the white inside of its mouth. Confines itself to holes and crevices in coral reefs ranging in depth from 10-25 m. Feeds on small fish.

Starry moray *Gymnothorax nudivomer*

Attains 100 cm. The main distinguishing feature of this moray is the bright yellow inside of its mouth. The body is a yellowish-brown with numerous close-set, small, irregular white spots anteriorly. The spots gradually become larger towards the tail and are rimmed with dark brown. Inhabits both coral and rocky reefs ranging in depth from 10-30 m. Common in the Aliwal Shoal area. Feeds primarily on fish and occasionally on octopus and crustaceans.

Geometric moray *Siderea grisea*

Attains 38 cm. This is a widespread and common species. A small moray, distinguished by its brownish head with conspicuous lines of small black dots. The body is lilac with brown marbling. Juveniles tend to be paler and have a lilac head. Ranges from rocky shores to deeper offshore rocky and coral reefs. Feeds mainly on small fish and crustaceans.

Catfishes – Family Ariidae

Natal seacatfish *Galeichthys* sp.

Attains 45 cm. Most catfishes live in fresh water but a few species occur in the sea. Their bodies are elongated and scaleless, and their heads are flattish. The dorsal fin and pectoral fins each bear a serrated, venomous spine. They are bottom-feeders and use the sensory barbels on their lower jaw to detect food. The Natal seacatfish is a newly identified species, as yet unnamed. The general body colour is purple-brown and the underside is pale. It is similar in appearance to the white seacatfish which is common off the Eastern Cape coast. Frequents shallow coastal waters off KwaZulu-Natal and feeds on small fish and crabs.

Honeycomb moray

Blackcheek moray

Guineafowl moray

Starry moray

Geometric moray

Natal seacatfish

Lizardfishes – Family Synodontidae

Variegated lizardfish (Reef lizardfish) *Synodus dermatogenys (*formerly *S. variegatus)*

Attains 22 cm. Lizardfishes are small, cylindrically shaped, bottom-dwelling reef fish. They have a reptile-like head with a large mouth full of slender, sharp teeth. Voracious predators of small fish and crustaceans, they lie in wait on the reef, ready to ambush passing prey. They are characteristic in the way they dash off when disturbed and then come to an abrupt halt. The variegated lizardfish is a common species, identified by the five or six red-brown vertical bars that intersect a red horizontal broken band on the flanks. Immediately below this broken band is a line of whitish dots. Colour can vary. Occurs on coral and rocky reefs, and is found singly or in pairs.

Halfbeaks – Family Hemiramphidae

Tropical halfbeak (Insular halfbeak) *Hyporhamphus affinis*

Attains 26 cm. Halfbeaks are a small family of elongated, slender, silvery fish with small mouths and spike-like lower jaws. They are surface-dwelling fish, shoaling in shallow bays, lagoons and along the lee of reefs. Able to skip along the surface when chased by a predator or disturbed by a vessel. Diet consists of algae, zooplankton and small fish. The tropical halfbeak is bluish on top with a greenish-silver underside, and a silvery stripe along the sides of the body. Ranges from Durban northwards.

Pineapplefishes – Family Monocentridae

Pineapplefish *Monocentris japonicus*

Attains 17 cm. These small fishes are encased with enlarged, solid scales that form a rough protective armour; the scales are yellow with black edging. They have a light-producing organ on the side of the lower jaw. The light is produced by luminescent bacteria; its purpose, however, is unknown. A widespread but uncommon fish that inhabits both coral and rocky reefs and protected rocky shores in depths ranging from 2-100 m. Found in holes and caves in the reef during the day, emerging at night to feed on small invertebrates. Occurs singly or in small groups.

Squirrelfishes and Soldierfishes – Family Holocentridae

Squirrelfishes and soldierfishes are medium-sized fish with oblong bodies and large eyes, and are frequently reddish in colour. Their scales are large and rough, and the fins very spiny. Many species are similar in appearance. The distinguishing feature between the two groups is the large, sharp, defensive spine which is found at the base of the gill plate in squirrelfish, but lacking in soldierfish. They generally shelter in caves, under ledges or among dense coral growth during the day, emerging at night to feed.

Tailspot squirrelfish *Sargocentron caudimaculatum*

Attains 25 cm. Overall reddish body with silver-edged scales and a silvery-white spot on upper tail base. A common squirrelfish found on coral and rocky reefs at depths of 10-30 m. Generally occurs singly and shelters in or near the reef during the day, preying on larvae and small crustaceans at night.

Crown squirrelfish *Sargocentron diadema*

Attains 20 cm. Distinguished by the alternating broad red and narrow silvery-white horizontal stripes on its body. A common species, inhabiting rocky shores and coral and rocky reefs to depths of 40 m. Often observed singly or in small groups, drifting close to the reef or peering out from its shelter. Feeds primarily on crustaceans at night.

Sabre squirrelfish (Long-jawed squirrelfish) *Sargocentron spiniferum*

Attains 45 cm. Uncommon, and one of the largest and most striking of squirrelfishes. Recognised by its deep body and steep sloping forehead. The body is overall red with scales edged in silver. The fins are reddish yellow. Generally occurs only on coral reefs to depths of 30 m. A solitary species, usually seen lurking in caves or crevices. Preys on crabs and shrimps during nocturnal feeding.

Variegated lizardfish

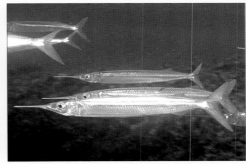

Tropical halfbeak

Pineapplefish

Tailspot squirrelfish

Crown squirrelfish

Sabre squirrelfish

Spotfin squirrelfish (Bloodspot squirrelfish) *Neoniphon sammara*

Attains 30 cm. This species has a slender body and a rather pointed head. The body is silvery with numerous thin reddish horizontal stripes. The dorsal area and inner margins of the tail are yellowish and the forward portion of the spinous dorsal fin has a large dark red spot. Outer margins of the tail, soft dorsal and anal fins are reddish. One of the most common squirrelfishes found on shallow tropical reefs. Often occurs near branching corals. Usually only observed from Inhaca Island northwards. Feeds on crustaceans at night.

Blotcheye soldier (Red soldierfish) *Myripristis murdjan*

Attains 27 cm. Recognised by the black edge to the gill covers and dark blotch above the eye. Body is silvery pink with red-edged scales. A very common soldierfish occurring in depths of 5-40 m on coral and rocky reefs. Often found in small groups hiding in caves, under ledges or drifting in the vicinity of its shelter. Diet consists of juvenile fish, larvae and crustaceans. Similar in appearance to several other related species.

Pale soldier (Finspot soldier) *Myripristis melanosticta*

Attains 30 cm. Distinguished by its silvery-white body with large red-edged scales; the head is dark red, and the tail and the soft dorsal and anal fins are dark red with white margins and black tips. An uncommon species which inhabits coral and rocky reefs deeper than 20 m. Generally observed in the open near its shelter during the day. Ranges from the Durban area northwards and feeds on crustaceans and larvae at night.

Trumpetfishes – Family Aulostomidae

Trumpetfish *Aulostomus chinensis*

Attains 80 cm. Trumpetfishes are unusually shaped, having a long thin body and a trumpet-like mouth giving a stick-like appearance. A single species occurs in the western Indian Ocean. Its colour varies and can be either yellow, blue-grey or reddish brown. A common fish found on shallow and deep coral and rocky reefs. A voracious predator that glides stealthily across the reef, sometimes in a head-down fashion in search of prey such as small fish. Often conceals itself behind larger fish or amongst shoaling fish when stalking prey. Capable of changing colour to blend with background.

Flutemouths – Family Fistulariidae

Smooth flutemouth (Cornetfish) *Fistularia commersonii*

Attains 150 cm. Flutemouths, or cornetfishes, as they are known in some regions, are extremely long, thin-bodied fishes with an extended tubular snout and a long whip-like tail. They feed by sucking in small invertebrates and fish in pipette-like fashion. The smooth flutemouth is greenish on the upper body shading to silvery white below, with two blue stripes or rows of blue spots on its back. A free-swimming fish, often seen hovering over reefs and seagrass beds. It is able to suddenly assume a dark barred pattern when swimming close to the bottom. Occurs solitarily or in small groups, ranging in depth from 1-100 m. A common species found throughout the Indo-Pacific.

Flagtails – Family Kuhliidae

Barred flagtail *Kuhlia mugil*

Attains 20 cm. Flagtails are small, compressed, silvery fishes which have a deeply notched dorsal fin and a forked tail. They inhabit shallow rocky shores and estuaries, and even enter fresh water. The barred flagtail has distinctive black and white barring across its tail. This common fish tends to shoal in turbulent areas by day, dispersing at night to feed on free-swimming crustaceans. Juveniles often congregate in tidal pools.

Spotfin squirrelfish

Blotcheye soldier

Pale soldier

Trumpetfish

Smooth flutemouth

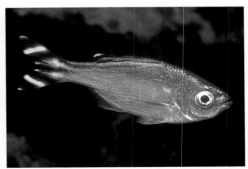

Barred flagtail

Scorpionfishes – Family Scorpaenidae

Scorpionfishes are a group of rather spiny and often bizarre-looking fish that include several species with defensive venomous fin spines. Wounds from touching the ends of these sharp spines can cause severe pain. Treatment of a wound entails applying an extremely hot poultice for at least 30 minutes to break down the powerful protein toxin. Scorpionfishes are largely solitary, bottom-dwelling reef fishes that rely on their camouflage to avoid detection while they lie in ambush for small fish. The exceptions are the various species of lionfishes which tend to be free-swimming.

Devil firefish (Lionfish) *Pterois miles*

Attains 30 cm. A bizarre-looking fish with large, feather-like dorsal and pectoral fins. The body and head are crossed with alternate thick and thin red bands interspaced with white. When threatened it raises its venomous dorsal spines in defence. A free-swimming species, encountered on shipwrecks and beneath overhangs on coral and rocky reefs, either solitarily or in groups. Juveniles are occasionally found in tidal pools. Primarily a nocturnal predator of small fish.

Broadbarred firefish (Spotfin lionfish) *Pterois antennata*

Attains 20 cm. Similar to the more common devil firefish, but the red bands on the body are wider and less numerous. The white rays of the pectoral fins are very elongated and the tentacle above each eye is usually long and cross-banded. The dorsal spines are poisonous. Usually found under ledges or in holes by day, but actively hunts for small fish at night. Ranges from Durban northwards and occurs on coral and rocky reefs to a depth of 50 m.

Stonefish *Synanceia verrucosa*

Attains 35 cm. This elaborately camouflaged, grotesque-looking fish is distinguished from the other scorpionfishes by its larger head, upturned mouth, squatter body and large, fan-like pectoral fins. The dorsal spines are extremely venomous. Normally found in shallow water where it lies in wait, ready to ambush small fish. Often partly buries itself in coral rubble or sand, making it almost impossible to detect. Should a stonefish be accidentally stepped on, it will erect its dorsal spines in defence.

Raggy scorpionfish *Scorpaenopsis venosa*

Attains 35 cm. An elaborately camouflaged bottom-dwelling fish which is difficult to detect as it blends so well with its surroundings. Often mistaken for a stonefish, but the mouth and pectoral fins are smaller and the body is less squat. This species has a variegated colour pattern and the colour can be altered to suit its surroundings. Skin flaps and tentacles decorate the head and body. The dorsal spines are extremely venomous. Inhabits coral and rocky reefs ranging in depth from 2-30 m. Lies on the reef, ready to ambush small fish and crustaceans.

Paperfish (Leaf fish) *Taenianotus triacanthus*

Attains 10 cm. A member of the scorpionfish family, this uncommon, odd-looking fish has a thin body resembling a leaf or a piece of paper as it sits passively on the reef, rocking from side to side with the surge. Colour varies from light tan to reddish yellow to cream. It can be easily overlooked due to its camouflage. The dorsal spines of the paperfish are not poisonous, and the skin is periodically shed. Inhabits shallow coral and rocky reefs, and inshore areas. Ranges from southern KwaZulu-Natal northwards. Preys on small fish and crustaceans.

Soapfishes – Family Grammistidae

Sixstripe soapfish *Grammistes sexlineatus*

Attains 15 cm. Soapfishes are small rockcod-like fishes that produce a slimy layer of toxic mucus on their skin to protect them from predators. The sixstripe soapfish is dark brown to black with horizontal yellow stripes along the body. Relatively uncommon, this solitary, secretive fish inhabits rocky shores, shallow coral and rocky reefs and tidal pools where it is found under ledges and in holes. A nocturnal predator of small fish and crustaceans.

Devil firefish

Broadbarred firefish

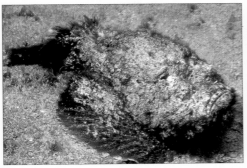

Stonefish

Raggy scorpionfish

Paperfish

Sixstripe soapfish

Rockcods – Family Serranidae

Subfamily Anthiinae

Goldies, or basslets, as they are known in most other countries, are a sub-family of the rockcods *(see page 28)*. These small, brightly coloured fishes move in large shoals above the reef in search of zooplankton. Males usually have extended filaments on the dorsal and caudal fins and are more colourful than the females. Most goldies start their reproductive lives as females. Harems are formed and the dominant female develops into a male which then mates with the other females.

Harlequin goldie *Pseudanthias connelli*

Attains 11 cm. The male is very striking, with the front half of the body being brownish black on top and whitish underneath, while the rear half is bluish purple. A diffused white horizontal line divides the dark and pale areas. Underwater the bluish-purple colour appears much duller. Females are plain in comparison, being overall brownish orange with a pale underside. The tips of the tail are distinctly rounded. Endemic to the KwaZulu-Natal coast, this uncommon goldie is only found in depths below 25 m on shipwrecks in the Durban and Aliwal Shoal areas. To the author's knowledge, this species has not yet been sighted on a reef. First discovered in 1986 by Dr Alan Connell, a local CSIR scientist. Feeds on zooplankton.

Silverstreak goldie (Red-bar anthias) *Pseudanthias cooperi*

Attains 10 cm. The female has a reddish-brown upper body, light brown flanks and a pale underside. The male has a reddish head, tail and dorsal fin with a pinkish body and a pale underside. Underwater the female appears reddish purple and the male pale purple. Both sexes have a pale grey stripe below the eye. During displays with females, the male exhibits a distinctive red blotch on the side of its body. Inhabits coral and rocky reefs at depths of 15-30 m and occurs in small shoals along the edges of reefs. Feeds on zooplankton.

Sea goldie (Goldie, Lyretail anthias) *Pseudanthias squamipinnis*

Attains 10 cm. The most common and abundant of all goldies. The female is overall orange-gold with two iridescent blue stripes extending backwards at an angle from the eye, and a blue ring around the top half of the eye. The male is reddish overall with yellowish flanks and has an extended third dorsal spine. Underwater the male appears purplish with pale yellow flanks. Males are larger than females. Ranges from tidal pools to coral and rocky reefs, where they are often seen shoaling in large numbers just above the reef. Feeds on zooplankton.

Harlequin goldie (male)

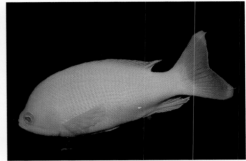

Harlequin goldie (female)

Silverstreak goldie (male)

Silverstreak goldie (female)

Sea goldie (male)

Sea goldie (female)

Threadfin goldie (Threadfin anthias) *Nemanthias carberryi*

Attains 7 cm. Males have an extended lower lobe to the caudal fin, a protrusion on the upper lip, and appear yellowish green underwater. Females are overall brownish orange in colour; both sexes have a green ring around the eye and yellow and purple lines extending backwards at an angle from the eye. A relatively common goldie, found on coral and rocky reefs in depths ranging from 10-30 m. Occurs in small groups along the edges of reefs. Feeds on zooplankton.

Yellowtail goldie (Yellowback anthias) *Pseudanthias evansi*

Attains 9 cm. One of the most striking goldies with its bright yellow back, tail and dorsal fins, and purple body. A common and abundant species found on coral reefs where it forms large aggregations on outer reef slopes and drop-offs. Only occasionally seen on the Maputaland reefs. Ranges in depth from 4-40 m, and feeds on zooplankton.

Rockcods – Family Serranidae

Rockcods vary from small to very large, and are characterised by their strong, robust bodies, rounded pectoral fins and large mouths. They commence maturity as females but change sex later in life. They are solitary, carnivorous reef-dwellers, often seen in caves or under ledges during the day. Many are strongly territorial and inquisitive. Prey is drawn whole into their gullets by the powerful suction created when they open their large mouths.

Peacock rockcod *Cephalopholis argus*

Attains 50 cm. An attractive fish with numerous dark-edged blue spots on a yellowish-brown body. A fairly uncommon rockcod which inhabits coral reefs but is occasionally found in the Aliwal Shoal area. Feeds mainly on cave-dwelling reef fish and crabs. Juveniles are sometimes seen in tidal pools along rocky shores.

Redmouth rockcod *Aethaloperca rogaa*

Attains 60 cm. This deep-bodied rockcod is overall dark brown to black in colour and often has a whitish bar centred on the abdomen. The inside of the mouth is red, hence its common name. A widespread but uncommon species, generally confined to coral reefs and usually observed in the vicinity of caves. Ranges in depth from 10-40 m. Feeds primarily on crustaceans and small shoaling fish associated with caves.

Coral rockcod (Coral hind) *Cephalopholis miniata*

Attains 40 cm. One of the most strikingly coloured rockcods with its orange-red to reddish-brown body covered with numerous blue spots. Capable of assuming an additional pattern of pale, irregular crossbars on the body, depending on its behavioural mood. A relatively common inhabitant of shallow coral reefs, but only occasionally seen on rocky reefs. Usually found near caves or under ledges. Feeds primarily on crustaceans and small fish.

Threadfin goldie (male)

Threadfin goldie (female)

Yellowtail goldie

Peacock rockcod

Redmouth rockcod

Coral rockcod

Duskyfin rockcod *Cephalopholis nigripinnis*

Attains 25 cm. A small rockcod, which is reddish overall with numerous small orange-red spots on the head, upper body and median fins. It appears dark reddish brown underwater. A widespread and common species associated with coral reefs. Often observed resting on the reef in a secluded spot, ready to ambush its prey. Ranges in depth from 5-40 m. Feeds mainly on small fish, but crabs, worms and shrimps are also eaten.

Redbarred rockcod (Blacktip grouper) *Epinephelus fasciatus*

Attains 35 cm. A small rockcod distinguished by the five broad red bars on a grey or sometimes orange-red body. Capable of assuming dark or pale colour variations, depending upon behavioural mood. Fairly common on coral and rocky reefs in depths to 30 m. Often found lying between coral heads, waiting to pounce on unsuspecting fish or crustaceans.

Yellowbelly rockcod *Epinephelus marginatus*

Attains 150 cm. One of the larger members of the rockcod family, recognised by the irregular green-white blotches on a brown body and yellow belly. A common inhabitant of rocky shores and coral and rocky reefs. Tends to be rather sluggish and is frequently seen resting on the reef or sand bottom. Crayfish are particularly favoured as food and are swallowed whole.

Brindle bass (Giant grouper) *Epinephelus lanceolatus*

Attains 270 cm (400+ kg). This is the largest member of the rockcod family and the biggest Indo-Pacific bony reef fish. Adults are a mottled, dark greyish brown and have a distinctive rounded tail. Juveniles have irregular dark brown and yellow bars. Inhabits deep estuaries, large caves, rocky and coral reefs and shipwrecks; known to occur to a depth of at least 100 m. Juveniles may occur in brackish water. Strongly territorial and potentially dangerous to divers. Feeds on various species of fish, small sharks, stingrays and spiny lobsters.

Yellowtail rockcod (Blue-and-yellow grouper) *Epinephelus flavocaeruleus*

Attains 90 cm. The juvenile phase is very striking with a dark blue body and bright yellow fins. With growth, the yellow areas disappear and the body becomes either totally black or a greyish mottle. Rather uncommon, it ranges from the Eastern Cape northwards. Juveniles frequent shallow reefs, whereas adults occur on reefs to depths of 150 m. Drifts near the bottom but is also observed in open water well above the reef. Feeds on reef fish, crabs, crayfish and squid.

Bigspot rockcod (Snubnose grouper) *Epinephelus macrospilos*

Attains 51 cm. A relatively common rockcod distinguished by the numerous close-set, dark brown spots with pale interspaces on the head and body. Inhabits coral and rocky reefs from the rocky shores to depths of 30 m. Often seen lying on an elevated rock or coral head waiting to pounce on unsuspecting small fish and crustaceans.

Duskyfin rockcod

Redbarred rockcod

Yellowbelly rockcod

Brindle bass

Yellowtail rockcod

Bigspot rockcod

Halfmoon rockcod *Epinephelus rivulatus*

Attains 35 cm. This small rockcod has a variable colour pattern but typically has five irregular, broad, dark brown bars on a brownish-orange body. A fairly common rockcod that frequents rocky reefs, particularly with weedy bottoms at depths of 15-80 m. This well-camouflaged fish often lies on the reef, waiting to ambush small fish and crustaceans.

Potato bass *Epinephelus tukula*

Attains 200 cm (100 kg). One of the largest members of the rockcod family. Distinguished by the large, widely spaced, dark brown spots on a greyish body. Shelters in caves but is territorial over large areas of the reef. An inquisitive fish which can be a nuisance to divers if accustomed to hand feeding. Should be treated with respect. Feeds on a variety of reef fish, stingrays, crabs and crayfish. Occurs on shallow to deep rocky and coral reefs.

Marbled leopardgrouper (Marbled coralgrouper) *Plectropomus punctatus*

Attains 90 cm. This medium-sized rockcod has a more tropical distribution. It has a purplish-brown body with irregular pale mottling, and deep blue margins to fins and tail. Capable of considerable change in colour. An inquisitive fish which boldly approaches divers when they enter its territory. Inhabits mainly coral reefs at depths of 5-30 m. Feeds on fish and crustaceans.

Yellow-edge lyretail (Swallowtail rockcod) *Variola louti*

Attains 80 cm. One of the most striking and graceful rockcods. Distinguished by its red body covered with numerous purple spots, the yellow margins to its fins and a deeply forked tail. Light coloured markings on body can occur, depending upon behavioural mood. Juveniles are very different in colour to adults. Their body is brownish orange above and whitish below, with an irregular black stripe from eye to base of tail. Numerous small blue spots cover the flanks. An inhabitant of shallow to deep coral reefs and occasionally rocky reefs. Feeds primarily on cave-dwelling fish.

Dottybacks – Family Pseudochromidae

Dutoiti *Pseudochromis dutoiti*

Attains 9 cm. Dottybacks are small, elongate fishes, often brilliantly coloured. They are very shy, highly territorial and confine themselves to crevices in the reef, occasionally venturing out to feed on small crustaceans and plankton. The female deposits a ball of eggs on the reef which are guarded by the male. The dutoiti is the most common dottyback along the East Coast. This striking fish has a reddish-brown body with a V-shaped neon line running from the head along the length of its back. Inhabits rocky shores and shallow rocky and coral reefs, and occurs singly or in pairs.

Bigeyes – Family Priacanthidae

Crescent-tail bigeye *Priacanthus hamrur*

Attains 45 cm. Bigeyes typically have very large eyes, a relatively deep and compressed body and a large downturned mouth. Most are deep-water dwellers, hiding in caves in the reef during the day. They move away from their shelter at night to prey on zooplankton and crustaceans. The crescent-tail bigeye has a distinctive forked tail and is able to change colour from a deep coppery red to a blotched red and silver or a pinkish silver. It is common on shallow coral reefs and is occasionally seen on rocky reefs. It occurs singly, but sometimes forms a large compact group that drifts above the reef during the day.

Halfmoon rockcod

Potato bass

Marbled leopardgrouper

Yellow-edge lyretail

Dutoiti

Crescent-tail bigeyes

Cardinalfishes – Family Apogonidae

Cardinalfishes are a large family of small, colourful fish characterised by two separate dorsal fins that are usually carried erect, large eyes and distinct markings of stripes or spots. There are many similar species, which makes identification difficult. They inhabit both coral and rocky reefs, and some frequent tidal pools. These fish are slow-moving, nocturnal feeders, and usually hide in caves and crevices during the day. Occasionally they congregate in small to large groups in the open, close to their shelter. The males of some species incubate the eggs in their mouths.

Short-tooth cardinal (Goldbelly cardinalfish) *Apogon apogonides*

Attains 10 cm. Distinguished by its brownish-mauve back, shading to yellow on the lower flanks, with two broken blue stripes or spots on the sides of the body. Relatively common, it occurs on shallow and deep reefs and is sometimes seen on shipwrecks. Tends to congregate in shoals during the day. Feeds on zooplankton and small invertebrates.

Bandtail cardinal (Ringtailed cardinalfish) *Apogon aureus*

Attains 12 cm. An attractive species which features a golden body with short horizontal blue stripes above and below the eye. Juveniles less than 5 cm in size have a distinctive black band around the base of the tail, but this disappears with age. Common on shallow coral and rocky reefs, occurring singly or in small groups. Preys on small invertebrates and zooplankton.

Spinyhead cardinal (Iridescent cardinalfish) *Apogon kallopterus*

Attains 15 cm. A common, widely distributed species, distinguished by its overall brown body with a black, mid-lateral stripe from snout to tail, and a black spot at base of tail. Inhabits coral and rocky reefs in depths ranging from 10-30 m. Occurs singly or in small groups, and feeds on small invertebrates and zooplankton.

Wolf cardinalfish *Cheilodipterus artus*

Attains 22 cm. This is one of the largest cardinalfishes, distinguished by the eight to ten dark brown longitudinal stripes on a whitish body. Occurs on coral and rocky reefs at depths of 10-25 m. Found in caves and under ledges and is usually seen singly or in pairs. Its prey consists of small invertebrates and zooplankton.

Rubberlips and Grunters – Family Haemulidae

Rubberlips and Grunters are a family of small- to medium-sized fishes distributed worldwide. They resemble snappers, but differ in having a smaller mouth, thicker lips (especially the rubberlip species) and smaller teeth. Most have distinctive patterns, such as stripes or bands. Grunters sometimes grind their pharyngeal teeth together after being captured, producing a grunting sound. Some species of rubberlips undergo dramatic changes in colour and pattern with growth.

Lemonfish *Plectorhinchus flavomaculatus*

Attains 60 cm. Distinguished by its thick, fleshy lips, golden lines on head, and golden spots on a grey body. Juveniles differ as they only have horizontal golden lines on their body. This member of the rubberlip family is found on both rocky and coral reefs at depths of 5-30 m. A common and inquisitive fish, often seen lurking close to the reef. Preys mainly on invertebrates and small fish.

Oriental sweetlips *Plectorhinchus orientalis*

Attains 86 cm. One of the most strikingly coloured of the sweetlips family. Adults are whitish with horizontal black stripes extending to the belly. The stripes are wider and darker on the upper body. The fins are yellow, with large black spots on the tail, anal and rear of dorsal fins. Juveniles are dark brown with creamy blotches; they remain close to coral heads for protection and swim in a peculiar undulating fashion. Usually solitary, but can occur in large groups; found in depths of 2-25 m. Confined to coral reefs from central Mozambique northwards. Feeds on bottom-living invertebrates.

Short-tooth cardinal

Bandtail cardinal

Spinyhead cardinal

Wolf cardinalfish

Lemonfish

Oriental sweetlips

Blackspotted sweetlips *Plectorhinchus gaterinus*

Attains 45 cm. Distinguished by its whitish body and numerous black spots on the flanks and upper body. The fins are yellow with black spots on the anal, dorsal and caudal fins. Juveniles up to 12 cm have black stripes on the head and body which turn into spots with age. Often occurs in large groups under ledges or along coral slopes. Generally confined to coral reefs from Maputaland northwards. Feeds on bottom-living invertebrates.

Whitebarred rubberlip *Plectorhinchus playfairi*

Attains 90 cm. Easily recognised by its thick fleshy lips, four white vertical bars on a dark upper body and pale underside. Commonly observed in the Sodwana Bay area, this solitary fish inhabits both coral and rocky reefs from the inter-tidal zone to deep offshore reefs. Feeds primarily on small invertebrates and occasionally small fish.

Piggy (Pinky) *Pomadasys olivaceum*

Attains at least 15 cm. An inconspicuous fish with an overall silvery, olive-grey body with a pinkish sheen on the upper flanks. This is one of the smaller grunters and occurs in large, dense shoals around the edges of reefs, deep-water pinnacles and on shipwrecks. Heavily preyed upon by pelagic fish, sharks and dolphins. Often caught by fishermen for bait. Juveniles usually inhabit rocky shores. Preys mainly on shrimps and other sand-dwelling invertebrates.

Spotted grunter *Pomadasys commersonnii*

Attains 80 cm. One of the larger grunters, with a distinctive long, sloping forehead and an elongate body. The overall colour is silvery with black spots on the sides and back. An abundant species which is found in estuaries and lagoons, along sandy shores and near shipwrecks. Feeds by blowing a jet of water down the holes of burrowing prawns and worms, forcing out its prey.

Striped grunter *Pomadasys striatum*

Attains 22 cm. Overall silvery-brown with three distinctive brown stripes along upper flanks. A common grunter found along protected rocky shores and coral and rocky reefs to a depth of 40 m. Often occurs in small shoals around scattered reef areas. Feeds on shrimps and crabs, capturing its prey in a manner similar to that of the spotted grunter.

Cavebasses – Family Dinopercidae

Cavebass *Dinoperca petersi*

Attains 60 cm. Cavebasses are closely related to rockcods. A single species occurs in the Indian Ocean. They are oval-shaped, have large eyes and are overall dark brown to black with numerous white specks on the body. Juveniles are a creamy colour with several dark vertical bars. Relatively common, it inhabits areas from rocky shores to offshore coral and rocky reefs. Found in caves and under ledges during the day, coming out at night to prey on crabs and shrimps.

Blackspotted sweetlips

Whitebarred rubberlip

Piggy

Spotted grunter

Striped grunter

Cavebass

Snappers – Family Lutjanidae

Snappers are a large family of medium-sized, predatory fishes which inhabit shallow, subtropical and tropical reefs, although the young sometimes live in estuaries. Many are strikingly patterned and coloured, and vary greatly in shape. They occur mostly in shoals, though some larger species may be solitary hunters and cave-dwellers. Feeding habits vary according to species.

Twinspot snapper *Lutjanus bohar*

Attains 75 cm. A fairly common, large, solitary fish. Adults are reddish brown with paler underside. Juveniles have two distinctive white spots just below the dorsal fin. Inhabits both coral and rocky reefs, ranging in depth from 10-70 m. Usually seen patrolling the mid-water area or hiding beneath overhangs. Preys on small reef fish, squid and crustaceans.

Humpback snapper *Lutjanus gibbus*

Attains 50 cm. The body colour of this deep-bodied snapper can change from deep red to silvery white, depending on behavioural mood. Found on shallow coral and rocky reefs, it occurs either solitarily or in shoals. Most active at night when it feeds on plankton and small invertebrates.

Bluebanded snapper (Bluelined snapper) *Lutjanus kasmira*

Attains 30 cm. This is one of the most colourful and common snappers along the East Coast. It has a yellow body with a pale underside and four horizontal, black-edged, blue stripes along the flanks and upper body. Often found in compact shoals drifting over shallow coral or rocky reefs to at least 60 m. Feeds mainly at night on crustaceans and small fish.

Dory snapper (Black-spot snapper) *Lutjanus fulviflamma*

Attains 35 cm. Generally whitish or pale yellow on flanks with a pale reddish head and back. Has a prominent black spot on the lateral line and several yellow horizontal stripes on the lower flanks. Generally a solitary fish that inhabits shallow reefs and rocky shores, with juveniles frequenting tidal pools. Occasionally seen swimming with a shoal of bluebanded snappers (*L. kasmira*). Feeds mainly on crustaceans. Can be confused with the one-spot snapper (*L. monostigma*) which is similar, but does not have yellow stripes on the lower flanks.

Yellow snapper (Bigeye snapper) *Lutjanus lutjanus*

Attains 30 cm. The distinguishing features of this snapper are a silvery-white body with a yellow stripe extending from the eye to the tail along the side of body, and a number of thinner yellow stripes below it. Above the lateral line there are a number of thin yellow to brown oblique lines angled backwards. Found either singly or in large shoals on coral reefs to a depth of at least 40 m. Often drifts over the reef in the company of one-spot and bluebanded snappers. A relatively common snapper, ranging from Maputaland northwards. Diet includes fish, shrimps and crabs.

Fusiliers – Family Caesionidae

Fusiliers are characterised by a slender, streamlined body, a deeply forked tail and bright colouration. They are closely related to snappers and often occur in large shoals, swimming over and between reefs. Their shoaling habit offers some protection against predatory gamefish, and they are often seen breaking the surface in an attempt to escape capture. Fusiliers are mid-water, zooplankton feeders. They occasionally swarm around divers as they swim past.

Blue-and-gold fusilier (Scissor-tailed fusilier) *Caesio caerulaureus*

Attains 30 cm. The most common of the fusilier species along the East Coast. The body is generally bluish green with a prominent yellow stripe along the flanks. The stripe can vary in width, and is sometimes blue-edged. Occurs over both coral and rocky reefs, and feeds on zooplankton.

Twinspot snapper

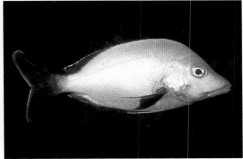

Humpback snapper

Bluebanded snappers

Dory snapper

Yellow snappers

Blue-and-gold fusiliers

Yellowback fusilier *Caesio xanthonota*

Attains 30 cm. One of the loveliest and most shapely of fishes. Easily recognised by its yellow back and blue flanks. Commonly observed in the Sodwana Bay area. Tends to shoal above and along the outer edges of coral reefs, feeding on zooplankton.

Neon fusilier (Bluestreak fusilier) *Pterocaesio tile*

Attains 25 cm. Recognised by the black stripe along the lateral line, with neon blue zone below it and a reddish underside. Rather uncommon, it tends to have a tropical distribution. Occasionally seen in the Sodwana Bay area. Preys on zooplankton.

Seabreams – Family Sparidae

Seabreams are an abundant family of fish in southern African waters and are popular linefish. They are characterised by their large heads and steep foreheads. Many have been found to change sex. Some start their lives as females and later change to male, while others start off as males and change to female with age. They are predominantly shoaling fishes, although some may congregate around rocky pinnacles. Feeding habits vary according to species.

Englishman *Chrysoblephus anglicus*

Attains 80 cm. A popular but depleted linefish which is endemic to the Mozambique and KwaZulu-Natal coasts. The vertical crossbars on its silvery body can vary from pale to dark pink. Inhabits reefs in depths ranging from 15-100 m, and occurs singly or in small groups. Sometimes forages in the sand for crustaceans by blowing into it to expose potential prey. Not easily approached underwater.

Slinger *Chrysoblephus puniceus*

Attains 60 cm. This important commercial linefish has an overall silvery-pink body and a conspicuous blue bar below the eye. Congregates in large shoals over offshore rocky reefs and pinnacles at depths of 20-100 m. Particularly common in the Aliwal Shoal area. A bottom-feeder of crustaceans and molluscs. This species undergoes a sex change from female to male.

Zebra *Diplodus cervinus*

Attains 50 cm. Distinguished by its silvery body and vertical black crossbars. A common species that occurs singly or in small shoals. It inhabits rocky shores as well as deeper rocky and coral reefs. Juveniles sometimes frequent tidal pools. Feeds on small crabs and worms.

Blacktail *Diplodus sargus capensis*

Attains 40 cm. This oval-shaped silver fish has a prominent black patch at the base of the tail. Juveniles have several thin vertical crossbars on the side of the body. Occurs in small shoals on shallow rocky and coral reefs and along rocky shores. Common along the entire African east coast. An omnivorous feeder of seaweeds, mussels and redbait.

Yellowback fusiliers

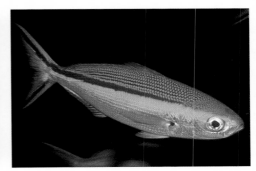

Neon fusilier

Englishman

Slinger

Zebra

Blacktail

German *Polyamblyodon germanum*

Attains 45 cm. A lesser known, but nevertheless common seabream. It has an overall silvery-grey colour. Occurs alone or in small groups and inhabits rocky reefs at depths of 12-30 m. Fairly common in the Aliwal Shoal area. Feeds on encrusting organisms such as redbait and small molluscs. Similar to the bronze bream (*P. grande*) which has a bluish-bronze colour.

Natal stumpnose *Rhabdosargus sarba*

Attains 80 cm. A widespread silvery seabream with many faint yellow horizontal lines over the body. Confined to shallow coastal waters, it generally lives close to the shoreline but occasionally ventures to deeper reefs. A bottom-feeder which uses its strong teeth to crush molluscs and crustaceans.

Cape stumpnose *Rhabdosargus holubi*

Attains 40 cm. Distinguished by its blunt head and silver body with a yellow stripe along the mid-line of the body. A common fish along the southern and eastern coast of South Africa. Adults frequent estuaries, rocky shores and deep reefs. Juveniles occur mainly in estuaries, where they graze on eelgrass. Adults feed on bottom-living invertebrates.

Bigeye stumpnose *Rhabdosargus thorpei*

Attains 50 cm. Similar in appearance to the Natal stumpnose (*R. sarba*) but has a broad golden band on the underside, and larger eyes. Often found shoaling in shallow coastal waters, usually over sandy bottoms. A bottom-feeder of molluscs and crustaceans.

Strepie (Karanteen) *Sarpa salpa*

Attains 30 cm. This member of the seabream family has longitudinal orange stripes on a silvery body. An abundant shoaling fish; favours cool water off rocky shores. More common off KwaZulu-Natal during winter and spring when spawning occurs. Adults feed almost exclusively on red seaweeds.

Emperors – Family Lethrinidae

Emperors are related to sweetlips and snappers. They generally lack bright colours and are confined to warm waters. Most species are capable of dramatically adopting a dark mottled or reticulate colour pattern, depending on behavioural mood. They are both shoaling and solitary fishes, found near sand and rubble slopes or around reef outcrops. All are carnivorous and feed on sand-dwelling invertebrates.

Glowfish *Gnathodentex aureolineatus*

Attains 30 cm. Distinguished by its silvery body with horizontal yellow stripes on flanks and a conspicuous bright yellow patch at the end of the dorsal fin. This approachable emperor is generally confined to coral reefs at depths of 10-20 m. Occurs singly or in loosely packed shoals which tend to drift above the reef. Preys on sand-dwelling invertebrates.

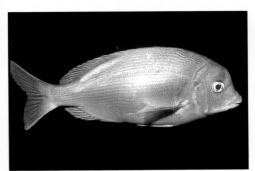

German

Natal stumpnose

Cape stumpnose

Bigeye stumpnose

Strepie

Glowfish

Yellowfin emperor *Lethrinus crocineus*

Attains 60 cm. Distinguished by its steep forehead, yellow fins and silvery yellow body, which becomes darker above and paler below. Occurs on coral and rocky reefs, and is often seen in the Sodwana Bay area. Frequently hovers in mid-water above the reef. Feeds on sand-dwelling invertebrates.

Blue emperor (Spangled emperor) *Lethrinus nebulosus*

Attains 75 cm. Has a long, sloping forehead and a rather pointed snout. The upper body colour is olive-green and the underside is pale. Each scale has a bluish centre. One of the largest and most common of emperors, it occurs singly or in loosely packed shoals near rocky and coral reefs at depths of 15-50 m. Diet consists of sand-dwelling invertebrates.

Spotcheek emperor (Redgill emperor) *Lethrinus rubrioperculatus*

Attains 40 cm. Distinguished by its pointed snout, brown to green body with blue tinges, and red spot on gill cover and pectoral base. A widespread and common emperor which occurs singly or in loosely packed shoals near coral reefs. Preys on sand-dwelling invertebrates.

Galjoen – Family Coracinidae

Banded galjoen *Coracinus multifasciatus*

Attains 30 cm. A small family, confined to the coastal waters of southern Africa and Madagascar. Generally found in turbulent water along rocky shores but can also occur on shallow offshore reefs. The banded galjoen is an abundant fish frequenting the warmer waters of southern Africa. Identified by its grey body with alternating wide and narrow vertical dark bands. Occurs singly or in small groups, and consumes a wide variety of invertebrates, including redbait.

Chubs (Rudderfish) – Family Kyphosidae

Blue chub (Highfin rudderfish) *Kyphosus cinerascens*

Can attain 70 cm. Chubs are plump fishes with noticeably small heads. They inhabit shallow, turbulent waters and feed exclusively on seaweed and redbait. They can suddenly adopt a white spotted pattern on the body, depending on their behavioural mood. The blue chub is overall greyish blue in colour and, compared to other related species, has a high soft dorsal fin. Sometimes it congregates in large numbers to graze on seaweed-covered rocks.

Stonebreams – Family Scorpididae

Stonebream *Neoscorpis lithophilus*

Can attain 50 cm. The stonebreams are closely related to the chub family and are represented by a single species in southern African waters. The stonebream is recognised by its kite-shape and silvery-grey colour. An endemic and abundant fish which is restricted to turbulent surf zones and rocky shores, where it feeds on seaweed.

Yellowfin emperor

Blue emperor

Spotcheek emperor

Banded galjoen

Blue chub

Stonebream

Batfishes – Family Ephippidae

Batfishes are characterised by a deep, compressed body with a short head and small mouth. These graceful shoaling fishes are often seen swimming near the surface above reefs and are occasionally seen breaking the surface with their dorsal fins. They swim with a distinctive, slow, waggling motion.

Orbicular batfish (Circular spadefish) *Platax orbicularis*

Attains 30 cm. Has a pale body with brown crossbars which fade with age, and a black blotch above the pelvic fin. Can be confused with the longfin batfish (*P. teira*) which has two black blotches between the pelvic and anal fins. Juveniles have long, exaggerated dorsal and anal fins. Feeds mainly on algae and small invertebrates.

Spadefish *Tripterodon orbis*

Attains 75 cm. A member of the batfish family, the spadefish has a reasonably large, compressed body which is silvery in colour with dark crossbars and a touch of yellow on the dorsal fin and tail. The crossbars disappear with age. Also a shoaling fish usually found close to shallow reefs. Diet includes mid-water invertebrates and encrusting reef organisms. Inquisitive fish easily approached by divers.

Moonies (Monos) – Family Monodactylidae

Natal moony *Monodactylus argenteus*

Attains 20 cm. Moonies are small, kite-shaped, silvery fish that occur in large dense shoals along sheltered rocky shores and in estuaries. They are tolerant of high and low salinity, and feed mainly on plankton. Juveniles have a yellow tip on the dorsal and anal fins. Adults generally have dusky tips. Similar to the Cape moony (*M. falciformis*) which has a dusky tip on only the dorsal and anal fins.

Goatfishes – Family Mullidae

Goatfishes are distinctive by their elongate bodies and whisker-like barbels that project from the lower jaw. These fishes are common in the shallows as well as on deeper reefs. Generally seen over sandy areas adjacent to reefs, busily probing the sand with their barbels in search of small crustaceans and molluscs. Goatfishes are occasionally followed by a lone kingfish hoping to prey on larger creatures disturbed from the seabed. Some species are solitary, whilst others form shoals.

Flame goatfish (Yellowfin goatfish) *Mulloides vanicolensis*

Attains 33 cm. Has a greyish-white body with a yellow back and a prominent horizontal yellow stripe along body. A common goatfish generally confined to shallow coral reefs but is occasionally seen in the Aliwal Shoal area. Unlike other species, it often forms large, dense shoals that swim slowly above the reef. Often seen shoaling with bluebanded snappers. Preys on bottom-dwelling crustaceans, worms and molluscs.

Twosaddle goatfish (Two-barred goatfish) *Parupeneus bifasciatus*

Attains 30 cm. Recognised by the two black bands across the body. Overall colour varies from greyish white to dusky red. Particularly common on the coral reefs and the rocky shores north of Maputaland. Occasionally seen in the Aliwal Shoal area. Occurs either singly or in pairs. Feeds on bottom-dwelling crustaceans, worms and molluscs.

Indian goatfish *Parupeneus indicus*

Attains 35 cm. Has a greyish-white body with yellow-edged scales, a yellow blotch in the middle of the back and a black dot at the base of the tail. A widely distributed goatfish which is particularly common on sandy areas along rocky shores. Also occurs on shallow coral and rocky reefs. Occurs singly or in pairs and feeds on bottom-living worms, crustaceans and molluscs.

Orbicular batfish

Spadefish

Natal moonies

Flame goatfish

Twosaddle goatfish

Indian goatfish

Band-dot goatfish (Long barbel goatfish) *Parupeneus macronema*

Attains 35 cm. Recognised by the broad, black horizontal stripe on the upper flanks and the black dot on the base of the tail. The body colour is usually dusky red. A common goatfish occurring solitarily or in pairs. Ranges from rocky shores to coral and rocky reefs at depths of 1-30 m. Preys on bottom-dwelling worms, crustaceans and molluscs.

Blacksaddle goatfish (Rosy goatfish) *Parupeneus rubescens*

Attains 45 cm. One of the largest and most common goatfishes. Body colour varies from salmon-pink to olive-green, and there is a distinctive black and white marking between dorsal fin and tail. Ranges from rocky shores to coral and rocky reefs at depths of 1-30 m and occurs singly or in small groups. Diet consists of bottom-dwelling crustaceans, worms and molluscs.

Sand Tilefishes – Family Malacanthidae

Sand tilefishes have elongate bodies and long continuous dorsal and anal fins. They live on sandy or rubble bottoms, often at the base of outer reef drop-offs. All species build burrows in the sand or under surface rock on sand, for shelter. They typically hover close to their refuge and if threatened make a rapid retreat to their burrows.

Stripetail tilefish (Quakerfish) *Malacanthus brevirostris*

Attains 30 cm. Distinguished by its long, slender, light grey body which tends to be yellowish green dorsally and yellowish above the eye with two black stripes on the tail. Only relatively common, it inhabits coral and rocky reefs, ranging in depth from 12-45 m. Occurs on open sand-rubble bottoms. Usually seen in pairs and lives in a burrow of its own construction. Feeds on small crustaceans.

Sand tilefish (Striped blanquillo) *Malacanthus latovittatus*

Attains 35 cm. This reasonably large species has a long slender body with the head and body blue, becoming whitish posteriorly, and a broad black mid-lateral stripe along body extending onto tail. Only occasionally observed, it inhabits shallow coral reefs ranging from Maputaland northwards. Frequents sandy areas or rubble near reefs. Typically hovers above the bottom and occurs solitarily or in pairs. Preys on small crustaceans.

Kobs – Family Sciaenidae

Common throughout the world, this large family of fish are highly valued as food. These large shoaling fishes are generally drab and dull-coloured, and have a rather robust and elongate body. They inhabit estuaries, shallow shores and deeper offshore reefs.

Daga kob *Argyrosomus japonicus* (formerly *A. hololepidotus*)

Attains 200 cm. This large predatory shoaling fish is silvery, with a pinkish sheen on the flanks, and has a distinctive row of pearly spots along the lateral line. A rather shy fish, only occasionally seen by divers. Regularly caught by commercial line fishermen. Ranges from shallow shores and estuaries to depths of 50 m. Feeds on small fish and crustaceans. Other similar related species are the squaretail kob (*Argyrosomus thorpei*), and the snapper kob (*Otolithes ruber*).

Slender baardman (Tasselfish) *Umbrina ronchus*

Attains 70 cm. A member of the kob family, it has a noticeable small tassel under the chin. Body colour varies from black to silver, depending on background. A rather sluggish fish, often seen hanging motionless below a rocky overhang or in small groups over sandy bottoms. Ranges in depth from 10-30 m and preys on bottom-dwelling invertebrates.

Band-dot goatfish

Blacksaddle goatfish

Stripetail tilefish

Sand tilefish

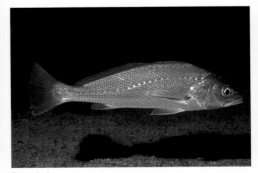

Daga kob

Slender baardman

49

Angelfishes – Family Pomacanthidae

Angelfishes are considered to be among the most beautiful and majestic of all reef fishes. These small to medium-sized, compressed, oval-shaped fishes are similar in habit and shape to butterflyfishes. However, a prominent, backward-projecting spine extending from the lower gill cover distinguishes them from butterflyfishes. They frequently have very striking colour patterns, and the juveniles of some species differ significantly in colour pattern from the adults. They occur both solitarily or in small groups. Most angelfishes are dependent on the presence of shelter in the form of boulders, caves and coral or rocky crevices. They are territorial and spend daylight hours near the bottom foraging for food. Their diet varies according to the species.

Emperor angelfish *Pomacanthus imperator*

Attains 40 cm. One of the most well-known and widespread angelfishes. The distinguishing colours of the adult are a blue body crossed with diagonal yellow lines, a yellow tail, a light blue mouth and a blue-edged black band over the eyes. The juvenile is strikingly different and has a pattern of concentric blue and white lines on a black body. Swims about reef with a graceful, unhurried movement. A relatively common angelfish found on both coral and rocky reefs, ranging in depth from 1-50 m. Juveniles are only occasionally found in tidal pools and tend to be rather timid. Adults are inquisitive and often swim right up to a diver. Large adults produce a loud grunting sound if threatened. Although generally seen alone, its partner is usually close by. Diet mainly consists of encrusting sponges, with algae and invertebrates also being eaten.

Semicircle angelfish *Pomacanthus semicirculatus*

Attains 50 cm. One of the most common and best-known angelfishes. This majestic and solitary species is friendly and easily approached. Adults are golden brown with numerous blue speckles on the body and fins. The fins are outlined in luminous blue. Juveniles are strikingly different, being black with a pattern of blue and white semi-circular lines. Juveniles frequent protected rocky shores and tidal pools and tend to be secretive; will disappear into a crevice if approached. Adults prefer depths ranging from 5-40 m and occur on coral and rocky reefs, often in caves or on shipwrecks. Juveniles feed on free-swimming animals such as small crustaceans, whilst adults feed on algae, sponges, sea squirts and invertebrates. Juveniles are very popular with marine aquarists.

Old woman angelfish *Pomacanthus rhomboides* (formerly *P. striatus*)

Attains at least 46 cm. Adults are overall grey-brown with a paler hind third. Juveniles are dark blue with a pattern of blue and white vertical lines with curved ends. Despite the adult's drab appearance, this angelfish, the most common of the East Coast angelfishes, has a friendly, inquisitive nature. Small groups often greet divers in mid-water above a reef. They seem to be attracted to divers' bubbles. Ranges from Knysna in the Eastern Cape northwards. Juveniles frequent tidal pools and rocky shores. They are solitary and rather timid, and tend to disappear into a crevice in the reef when threatened. Adults are found on shallow coral and rocky reefs and often congregate above reefs, in mid-water or even at the surface. Feeds on encrusting organisms such as sponges, sea squirts and coral polyps, and on invertebrates and plankton in mid-water. Juveniles are popular with marine aquarists.

Emperor angelfish (adult)

Emperor angelfish (juvenile)

Semicircle angelfish (adult)

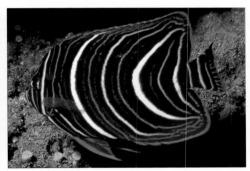

Semicircle angelfish (juvenile)

Old woman angelfish (adult)

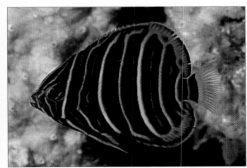

Old woman angelfish (juvenile)

Tiger angelfish *Apolemichthys kingi*

Attains 25 cm. A new angelfish, officially discovered by the author off Durban in 1984. A striking fish having a golden upper body with irregular vertical black markings and a white underside. Possibly endemic to the KwaZulu-Natal coast and inhabits deeper reefs ranging from 20-50 m. Relatively common on reefs from Durban to the Protea Banks, but only occasionally observed on the Maputaland reefs. A rather timid species that swims about the reefs, either singly or in pairs. Feeds on sponges and invertebrates.

Threespot angelfish *Apolemichthys trimaculatus*

Attains 25 cm. This brilliant yellow angelfish has distinctive blue lips and three black spots on the head. Juveniles resemble adults. Closely related to the tiger angelfish. Widespread and relatively common, it inhabits both coral and rocky reefs at depths of 10-30 m. Swims about reefs, usually singly, foraging for invertebrates, algae and sponges.

Royal angelfish (Regal angelfish) *Pygoplites diacanthus*

Attains 25 cm. This is the most strikingly coloured of the East Coast angelfishes. Has an overall orange colour with vertical black-edged blue bands across the body, and a yellow tail. Juveniles resemble adults. A shy species confined to coral reefs at depths of 10-20 m. Swims in and out of holes in the reef, either singly or in pairs. More abundant in tropical areas. Feeds on sponges and sea squirts.

Jumping bean (African pygmy angelfish) *Centropyge acanthops*

Attains 8 cm. One of the smallest and prettiest of southern African dwarf angelfishes. It has a distinctive blue body with an orange head and dorsal area. A rather timid but curious fish which is only occasionally observed. It inhabits shallow protected areas along rocky shores and on coral and rocky reefs at depths of 2-30 m. Prefers areas of rocky rubble or patches of staghorn coral where it darts in and out of holes. Feeds on small invertebrates.

Dusky cherub (Many-spined angelfish) *Centropyge multispinis*

Attains 14 cm. Recognised by its overall dark brown colour and brilliant blue edging to fins. This small, rather inconspicuous but approachable fish is the most common dwarf angelfish along the KwaZulu-Natal coast. Frequents rocky shores and shallow coral and rocky reefs. Usually occurs in family groups of between two and five, and can be observed darting in and out of crevices in the reef. Feeds on small invertebrates and algae.

Coral beauty (Two-spined angelfish) *Centropyge bispinosus*

Attains 10 cm. This pretty dwarf angelfish has its head and body outlined in deep purple; the flanks are reddish orange and are crossed with thin, vertical purple lines. Rather uncommon, it is generally confined to coral reefs but is occasionally seen in the Aliwal Shoal area. It ranges in depth from 15-40 m. Occurs singly or in pairs and darts in and out of holes in the reef. Feeds mainly on small invertebrates and algae.

Tiger angelfish

Threespot angelfish

Royal angelfish

Jumping bean

Dusky cherub

Coral beauty

Butterflyfishes – Family Chaetodontidae

Butterflyfishes are small, round, thin-bodied fish, each having a distinct colour pattern. Their small size (usually less than 20 cm) and slightly concave foreheads make them distinguishable from the larger, similarly shaped angelfishes which have rounded foreheads. Their eyes are generally concealed by dark bars on the head. These, and the false eyespots found near the tail on several species, are markings thought to confuse predators. At night they become inactive and may change colour and markings.

Threadfin butterflyfish *Chaetodon auriga*

Attains 20 cm. Distinguished by the herringbone pattern of grey lines on a white body, the yellow tail, dorsal and anal fins, and a black bar through the eye. Adults have a long filament extending from the soft dorsal fin. It is one of the more common and widely distributed butterflyfishes and inhabits rocky shores and coral and rocky reefs to depths of 30 m. Juveniles often frequent tidal pools. Feeds on algae and invertebrates.

Archer butterflyfish (Bennett's butterflyfish) *Chaetodon bennetti*

Attains 18 cm. A striking butterflyfish; the overall body colour is yellow with a large blue-edged black spot on the upper sides and a pair of long, narrow, curved blue bands extending backwards from the pectoral fin. Also has a blue-edged black bar through the eye. A common inhabitant of rich coral areas ranging from Inhaca Island northwards, at depths of 5-25 m. Flits about reef tops, usually in pairs. Feeds primarily on coral polyps.

Brownburnie (Chocolate butterflyfish) *Chaetodon blackburnii*

Attains 13 cm. One of the few dull-coloured butterflyfishes. The front of the body is yellow and the rear is dark brown. Several dark stripes radiate across the body and a black bar runs through the eye. A fairly common butterflyfish found along rocky shores and on coral and rocky reefs to depths of 30 m. Preys on small invertebrates.

Black-edged butterflyfish (African butterflyfish) *Chaetodon dolosus*

Attains 15 cm. Distinguished by its whitish body with rows of small black spots. The rear of the body and dorsal fin has a black band, and the tail is yellow. A black bar runs through the eye. A deep-water butterflyfish which is relatively common on reefs and shipwrecks along the KwaZulu-Natal coast in depths of 20-40 m. Occurs singly or in groups and is sometimes seen swimming well away from a reef. Feeds on algae and small crustaceans.

Saddled butterflyfish (Saddleback butterflyfish) *Chaetodon falcula*

Attains 20 cm. This striking butterflyfish has two distinctive dark saddle markings across the top of the body, hence its common name. The dorsal, anal and caudal fins are yellow with a black spot or bar at the base of the caudal fin. The body and head are white. A black bar runs through the eye and there are thin vertical lines on the body. Confined to coral reefs ranging from Inhaca Island northwards. Occurs at depths of 5-20 m and is common on tropical reefs. Often found in pairs or small groups. Swims about the reef foraging for coral polyps, crustaceans and algae.

Gorgeous gussy (Spotted butterflyfish) *Chaetodon guttatissimus*

Attains 12 cm. A delicately coloured butterflyfish with a pale yellow body and numerous rows of small black spots. A yellow-edged black bar runs through the eye. One of the smallest butterflyfishes; fairly common on coral reefs and occasionally sighted on rocky reefs, in depths of 1-25 m. Feeds on invertebrates, including coral polyps.

Threadfin butterflyfish

Archer butterflyfish

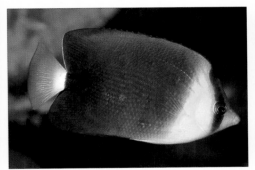

Brownburnie

Black-edged butterflyfish

Saddled butterflyfish

Gorgeous gussy

Whitespotted butterflyfish (Klein's butterflyfish) *Chaetodon kleinii*

Attains 14 cm. The overall colour of this butterflyfish is gold-yellow, with a white spot in the centre of each scale. A bluish-black bar runs through the eye. Similar in appearance to the limespot butterflyfish but does not have a black spot on its back. A common, widely distributed butterflyfish which inhabits rocky shores, coral and rocky reefs ranging in depth from 2-30 m. Encountered swimming about reefs, singly or in small groups. Feeds on algae and small invertebrates.

Halfmoon butterflyfish (Raccoon butterflyfish) *Chaetodon lunula*

Attains 20 cm. A distinctive fish with a yellowish-brown body and a complex arrangement of black bars and stripes. A noticeable black eye bar precedes a white bar which extends across the forehead. Juveniles have a black spot on the soft dorsal fin. A widely distributed species and a common resident of most shallow coral and rocky reefs, bays, harbours and tidal pools. Encountered either singly or in pairs, and occasionally in small groups. Preys on invertebrates and algae.

Pearly butterflyfish (Chevron butterflyfish) *Chaetodon madagascariensis*

Attains 15 cm. This uncommon butterflyfish has distinctive black chevron-like markings on a pearly white body, and an orange band at the rear of the body. Inhabits coral and rocky reefs ranging in depth from 2-30 m. Feeds on small invertebrates and algae.

Maypole butterflyfish (Meyer's butterflyfish) *Chaetodon meyeri*

Attains 17 cm. This striking butterflyfish has a distinctive disc-shape and colour pattern. The body is bluish white with curved black lines radiating across the body and fins. The fins and body margins are yellow. This species is confined to coral reefs where it lives in depths of 5-25 m. It occurs singly, in pairs or in small groups, and feeds almost exclusively on soft coral polyps. Juveniles often shelter in heads of branching coral.

Blackback butterflyfish *Chaetodon melannotus*

Attains 15 cm. This uncommon butterflyfish has a white body crossed by numerous thin diagonal black stripes and bordered by yellow dorsal, anal and caudal fins. The yellow head is divided by a black bar through the eye, and the rear of the back is blackish, hence its common name. Inhabits mainly coral reefs but occasionally ranges south to the Durban area. Occurs singly or in pairs in depths of 1-20 m. Feeds on invertebrates, coral polyps and algae.

Limespot butterflyfish (Teardrop butterflyfish) *Chaetodon unimaculatus*

Attains 19 cm. A brilliant yellow fish with a conspicuous black spot on its flanks and a black bar through the eye. Widely distributed, it is common on coral reefs and occasionally sighted on rocky reefs as far south as the Aliwal Shoal area. Frequently seen in pairs, it occurs at depths of 5-25 m. Feeds on algae, coral polyps and small invertebrates.

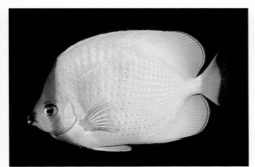

Whitespotted butterflyfish

Halfmoon butterflyfish

Pearly butterflyfish

Maypole butterflyfish

Blackback butterflyfish

Limespot butterflyfish

Doublesash butterflyfish *Chaetodon marleyi*

Attains 15 cm. A silvery-white fish with a yellowish brown bar through the eye and two broader bars extending across the flanks. The dorsal, pelvic and anal fins are also yellowish brown. Juveniles have a black spot on the soft dorsal fin. Endemic to southern Africa, this butterflyfish ranges from the Western Cape coast to the bay of Maputo. An attractive species commonly found in tidal pools and on offshore rocky reefs. Prefers colder water and is only occasionally seen along the Maputaland coast. Feeds on algae and small invertebrates.

Rightangle butterflyfish (Chevroned butterflyfish) *Chaetodon trifascialis*

Attains 18 cm. This butterflyfish has a more rectangular body shape. Its colour is white with narrow chevron markings on the sides. It has a prominent black bar through the eye, and the tail is mostly black except in juveniles where it is yellow. Inhabits coral reef areas at depths of 10-30 m and is associated with plate and branching corals. Only occasionally seen, this species is highly territorial and found singly or in pairs. Feeds exclusively on coral polyps and mucus.

Purple butterflyfish (Redfin butterflyfish) *Chaetodon trifasciatus*

Attains 15 cm. An attractive butterflyfish with narrow, slightly diagonal, purplish stripes on a yellow body. A yellow-edged black bar runs through eye. The base of the dorsal and anal fins have broad yellow-edged bands, which also appear across the middle of the caudal fin. Confined to coral reefs at depths of 5-25 m. Only occasionally seen on Maputaland reefs, but is common in tropical areas of the western Indian Ocean. Usually seen in pairs flitting about reef tops, feeding on coral polyps.

Vagabond butterflyfish *Chaetodon vagabundus*

Attains 23 cm. One of the largest butterflyfishes; has a white body and a herringbone pattern of grey lines on the flanks. The hind part of the body is yellow with vertical black bars across the eye and on the rear fringe of the body. A fairly common and widespread species inhabiting both coral and rocky reefs in depths of 1-30 m. Juveniles are often found in tidal pools. Can be confused with the threadfin butterflyfish (see page 54) which has similar colours. Preys on small invertebrates and algae.

Yellowhead butterflyfish *Chaetodon xanthocephalus*

Attains 20 cm. This large, handsome butterflyfish has a pearly-white body with several thin blackish chevron lines on the sides. The head, dorsal and anal fins are yellow and there is a white area at the base of the dorsal fin. Rather uncommon, it inhabits mainly coral reefs ranging from Maputaland northwards in depths between 5-25 m. Usually solitary but occasionally seen in pairs. Feeds on small invertebrates and algae.

Zanzibar butterflyfish *Chaetodon zanzibarensis*

Attains 12 cm. One of the smaller butterflyfishes. Overall colour is yellow with numerous narrow, dark, slightly curved stripes on sides. A black bar runs through the eye and there is a black spot on the upper flanks. Confined to rich coral reefs where it is relatively common. Ranges from Inhaca Island northwards in depths of 3-40 m. Often found close to staghorn corals. Usually solitary but occasionally seen in pairs. Feeds primarily on coral polyps.

Doublesash butterflyfish

Rightangle butterflyfish

Purple butterflyfish

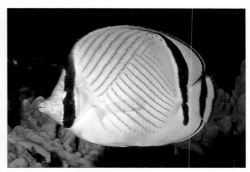

Vagabond butterflyfish

Yellowhead butterflyfish

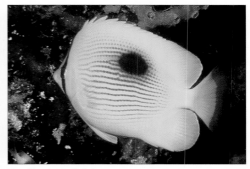

Zanzibar butterflyfish

Longnose butterflyfish *Forcipiger flavissimus*

Attains 16 cm. Widely distributed, this relatively common butterflyfish is distinguished by its bright yellow body, black and white head, and long tube-like snout which it uses to probe deep into crevices for small invertebrates. Frequents mainly coral reefs but does occur as far south as the Protea Banks. Ranges in depth from 10-30 m. Often seen swimming upside down when under a ledge or cave.

Brushtooth butterflyfish (Black pyramid butterflyfish) *Hemitaurichthys zoster*

Attains 16 cm. Easily recognised by its dark brown to black body with a broad white band in the middle. The dorsal spines over the white band are yellow, and the tail is white. Confined to coral reefs ranging from Maputaland northwards. Generally seen singly or in pairs on Maputaland reefs, but further north it is often observed in large groups swimming above the reef. Feeds on zooplankton in the mid-water zone.

Coachman (Threadback, Longfin bannerfish) *Heniochus acuminatus*

Attains 25 cm. A member of the butterflyfish family, the coachman is distinguished by its long white dorsal filament, two broad black diagonal bars across a white body, and the yellow soft dorsal, tail and pectoral fins. Sometimes confused with the moorish idol (see page 94) which is very similar in appearance. A similar related species is the schooling coachman *(H. diphreutes)* which ranges from Maputaland northwards. This is an approachable fish inhabiting coral and rocky reefs, and harbour areas at depths of 1-30 m. Occurs singly or in small groups. Juveniles sometimes remove parasites from other fish. Feeds on invertebrates and algae.

Masked coachman (Masked bannerfish) *Heniochus monoceros*

Attains 23 cm. Similar in shape and colour to the coachman described above, it can be distinguished by the protuberance just above the eye, and the dorsal and anal fins being more yellow. Not as common as the coachman, it generally occurs on coral reefs where it is found near gullies and caves in depths ranging from 2-25 m. Often observed in pairs and feeds on bottom-living invertebrates.

Knifejaws – Family Oplegnathidae

Knifejaws are a small family characterised by an oblong body, enlarged second dorsal fin and teeth fused to form a parrot-like beak. Adults are mostly drab and dark, but juveniles are often coloured with yellow and black crossbars.

Cape knifejaw *Oplegnathus conwayi*

Attains 90 cm. A robust fish with a pointed snout. Overall colour is silvery grey becoming darker on upper head and body. Common on coastal rocky reefs ranging from Cape Point to central KwaZulu-Natal. Has a powerful beak which it uses to nibble on seaweed, sponges and redbait. An inquisitive fish that readily approaches divers.

Natal knifejaw *Oplegnathus robinsoni*

Attains 60 cm. A robust, deep-bodied fish with an overall brown or grey-brown colour. Juveniles are bright yellow with black crossbars. Common on reefs ranging from southern KwaZulu-Natal to Mozambique. Particularly abundant on the Maputaland reefs. Can be readily approached by divers. Its powerful beak is used to scrape encrusting organisms off the reef.

Longnose butterflyfish

Brushtooth butterflyfish

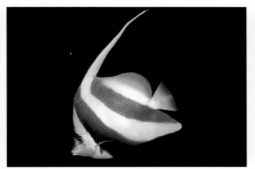

Coachman

Masked coachman

Cape knifejaw

Natal knifejaw

Kingfishes – Family Carangidae

Kingfishes are large, silvery fish characterised by their long, sickle-shaped pectoral fins, with dorsal and anal fins that extend to a powerful, deeply forked tail. They are open-water swimmers (pelagic fishes) but various species regularly visit reefs in small groups or large shoals in search of food. They are amongst the most active predators on the reef and can be seen swimming past with a sudden burst of speed as they chase smaller, unwary reef fish.

Bluefin kingfish *Caranx melampygus*

Attains 80 cm. A beautiful fish with a dusky green body, blue and black spots on the upper flanks, and vivid blue tail, dorsal and anal fins. Fairly common on shallow coral and rocky reefs. It hunts alone or in small groups, swimming just above the reef. Often follows goatfishes to find creatures disturbed from the sand during feeding. Preys on small fish, shrimps and squid.

Blacktip kingfish *Caranx heberi*

Attains 85 cm. Distinguished by its silvery-green body, yellow fins, and black-tipped tail and dorsal fin. Most frequently seen in summer from Durban northwards. Prefers open coastal waters where it hunts over shallow to moderately deep reefs, and feeds on small fish, shrimps and crabs. Usually occurs in small shoals.

Bigeye kingfish *Caranx sexfasciatus*

Attains 80 cm. A widespread and abundant species recognised by its dusky grey body, white-tipped second dorsal fin and large eyes. Hunts singly or in small shoals along reefs, preying on small fish, squid and mantis shrimps.

Hawkfishes – Family Cirrhitidae

Hawkfishes are small, colourful, bottom-dwelling reef fish characterised by a single, deeply notched dorsal fin with minute tassel-like filaments at the tip of each dorsal spine. They spend much of their time perched on coral heads, sponges or rocks, where they use their stout pectoral fins to balance themselves. They make periodic, quick dashes to capture prey such as small fish and crustaceans that come within range, returning inevitably to the same perch, hence the name hawkfish. The eyes are highly movable, giving the fish a wide range of vision.

Spotted hawkfish *Cirrhitichthys oxycephalus*

Attains 9.5 cm. A widely distributed hawkfish identified by the numerous dark red blotches on a pinkish body. Abundant on coral and rocky reefs at depths of 1-25 m. Generally solitary and strongly territorial. Preys on small fish and crustaceans.

Swallowtail hawkfish *Cyprinocirrhites polyactis*

Attains 14 cm. A relatively uncommon hawkfish distinguished by its mottled orange-brown body and deeply forked tail. Inhabits deeper coral and rocky reefs exposed to currents at depths ranging from 15-120 m. Particularly common in the Aliwal Shoal area. The only hawkfish that swims above the reef to feed on planktonic crustaceans and larvae.

Horseshoe hawkfish (Arc-eye hawkfish) *Paracirrhites arcatus*

Attains 14 cm. Rather uncommon, this hawkfish has a prominent yellow, red and pale blue U-shaped pattern next to the eye. Body is reddish with a white stripe along the rear half of the lateral line. Generally confined to coral reefs where it perches on branching coral heads. Ranges in depth from 10-30 m, and its diet consists of crustaceans and small fish.

Bluefin kingfish

Blacktip kingfishes

Bigeye kingfishes

Spotted hawkfish

Swallowtail hawkfish

Horseshoe hawkfish

Freckled hawkfish (Pixy hawkfish) *Paracirrhites forsteri*

Attains 22 cm. One of the largest and most common hawkfishes. Its colour is variable but generally the front half of the upper body is red, changing to black posteriorly with a broad white stripe along the side of the body. The head is always covered with red spots. Occurs mainly on coral reefs at depths of 6-25 m. Typically perches on branching coral heads. Feeds mainly on small fish and shrimps.

Longnose hawkfish *Oxycirrhites typus*

Attains 13 cm. This striking hawkfish has an extremely long snout, hence its common name. The body is whitish with horizontal and near vertical red bands forming a cross-hatch pattern. Uncommon to rare, it ranges from Aliwal Shoal northwards. Generally seen perched on black coral or gorgonians, usually at depths greater than 25 m. Feeds on small planktonic and bottom-living crustaceans.

Fingerfins – Family Cheilodactylidae

Fingerfins are a small family of bottom-dwelling fish that inhabit the cooler waters of southern Africa, New Zealand and Australia. They are characterised by an oblong body, enlarged pectoral fins used to balance themselves while 'lying' on the sea bed, and a small mouth with thick fleshy lips.

Twotone fingerfin *Chirodactylus brachydactylus*

Attains 40 cm. Distinguished by its reddish-brown body with paler underside and five white spots on the flanks. Endemic to southern Africa, this bottom-dwelling fish ranges from KwaZulu-Natal to Walvis Bay. Common on shallow rocky reefs, it spends much of its time resting on the bottom. Juveniles frequent tidal pools. Preys on small invertebrates.

Natal fingerfin *Chirodactylus jessicalenorum*

Can attain 75 cm. Has noticeably fleshy lips and an overall reddish-brown to dusky colour. Endemic to the KwaZulu-Natal coast, this common, bottom-dwelling fish inhabits reefs at depths of 3-30 m. Often observed resting on the reef, supported by its stout pectoral fins. Feeds on crabs, worms and other small invertebrates.

Sweepers – Family Pempheridae

Sweepers are small cryptic fishes with compressed bodies, large eyes and a single dorsal fin. They are largely nocturnal in habit, congregating in caves by day and dispersing at night to feed. Some species have luminescent organs.

Slender sweeper *Parapriacanthus ransonneti*

Attains 7,5 cm. This small sweeper is golden anteriorly and translucent reddish posteriorly. It inhabits coral and rocky reefs and shipwrecks to depths up to 30 m. By day it forms dense shoals and shelters in caves beneath overhangs. Disperses at night to feed on zooplankton.

Dusky sweeper *Pempheris adusta*

Attains 17 cm. The most common and widely distributed member of the family. It has a small, thin, hatchet-shaped body with large eyes and a shiny copper colour. This fish is identified from other similar species by the black margin to the anal fin. Usually congregates in small to large groups in caves and dark areas of shallow reefs and rocky shores by day. Preys on zooplankton at night.

Freckled hawkfish

Longnose hawkfish

Twotone fingerfin

Natal fingerfin

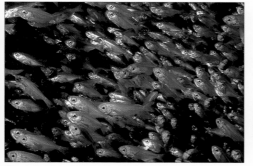

Slender sweepers

Dusky sweeper

Damselfishes – Family Pomacentridae

Damselfishes form one of the largest families of reef fish inhabiting warm, coastal waters. These small, oval-bodied fishes vary greatly in colour and pattern, and display interesting behavioural characteristics. Most species, especially algae-feeding species, are territorial and aggressive towards intruders, particularly when guarding their nesting sites. Some species occur singly or in small groups, whilst others form aggregations. They are often seen darting to and fro on a reef catching food in the passing current. Generally the drably coloured species feed mainly on algae, whereas many of the brightly patterned species and members of the genus *Chromis* feed on zooplankton. Female damselfishes lay their eggs on the substratum and are guarded by the male. Included in this family are the anemonefishes which live in symbiosis with large anemones.

Fourbar damsel (Natal sergeant) *Abudefduf natalensis*

Attains 17 cm. Distinguished by the four black vertical bars on a whitish body and the black margins on the tail. An abundant species along the KwaZulu-Natal coast, inhabiting shallow rocky and coral reefs, with juveniles more common in tidal pools. Strongly territorial, often seen in pairs or loosely packed groups swimming above the reef. Feeds on small crustaceans.

Dusky damsel (Yellow-tail sergeant) *Abudefduf notatus*

Attains 17 cm. Adults are dark brown with a blue spot on each scale, giving an overall bluish hue; five thin, white vertical bars cross the body; the tail is yellow. Juveniles are brownish with a grey underside and the white bars are sometimes not fully developed. A common damselfish inhabiting exposed rocky shores at depths of 1-12 m. Often occurs in tidal pools. Ranges from KwaZulu-Natal northwards. Occurs singly or in small groups and feeds on algae and small crustaceans.

Spot damsel (Black-spot sergeant) *Abudefduf sordidus*

Attains 20 cm. Has a distinctive black spot on the tail peduncle and five pale vertical bars on a grey-brown body. Juveniles are more grey with a black blotch on the dorsal area. Very common, especially along rocky shores exposed to wave action. Often found in tidal pools. Occurs singly or in small groups and is highly territorial. Feeds mainly on algae.

Sergeant major (Indo-Pacific sergeant) *Abudefduf vaigiensis*

Attains 20 cm. Colours can be variable, but most tend to be bluish grey with yellow upper flanks. There are five black vertical bars across the body. Abundant on nearly all inshore reefs, harbours and protected areas. Adults prefer deeper water to depths of 12 m where they often form small aggregations that swim above the reef. Juveniles frequent tidal pools. Very aggressive when guarding their eggs. Feeds on both small crustaceans and algae.

Nosestripe anemonefish (Skunk clown) *Amphiprion akallopisos*

Attains 9 cm. The body is overall pinkish with a white stripe along the dorsal surface from snout to tail. Females are usually larger than males. Lives in pairs or small groups among the stinging tentacles of large anemones and is aggressive towards other species. Inhabits coral reefs at depths of 2-30 m. The bodies of these fishes are coated with a special mucus which protects them from the stinging tentacles of the anemone. Lays its eggs in clusters on a rock at the base of the anemone. Feeds on filamentous algae and zooplankton.

Twobar anemonefish (Clownfish, Allard's anemonefish) *Amphiprion allardi*

Attains 14 cm. Distinguished by its deep body and rounded head profile. It has a blackish-brown body with two bluish-white vertical bars and orange-yellow fins. Females are larger than males. Inhabits mainly coral reefs and lives in pairs among the stinging tentacles of large anemones. It is immune to the stinging tentacles due to a protective mucus coating on its body. Aggressively protects the anemone from predators and will attack, and even bite, divers who venture too close, particularly during spawning. Lays its eggs in clusters on a rock at the base of the anemone. Feeds on filamentous algae and zooplankton.

Fourbar damsel

Dusky damsel

Spot damsel

Sergeant major

Nosestripe anemonefish

Twobar anemonefish

67

Bluespotted chromis *Chromis dasygenys*

Attains 12 cm. This damselfish has an overall blue-grey colour with a yellow forehead and upper flanks. A common damselfish, inhabiting rocky shores, coral and rocky reefs at depths of 1-15 m. Often found swimming in small groups just above the reef. Feeds on zooplankton.

Blue puller (Blue-green chromis) *Chromis viridis*

Attains 9 cm. The overall body colour is greenish yellow with a light bluish-green sheen to the scales and a blue line from eye to snout. Usually found with the very similarly coloured black-axil chromis (*C. atripectoralis*) which is slightly larger and has a black spot at the base of the pectoral fin. Confined to coral reefs ranging from Inhaca Island northwards. Often forms groups that swim above branching corals. Juveniles stay close to individual coral heads and when threatened, quickly retreat in unison into the safety of the coral branches. Feeds on zooplankton.

Chocolate dip (Two-tone chromis) *Chromis dimidiata*

Attains 7 cm. The front half of the body varies from black to dark brown, and the back half is white. This small damselfish is abundant on most coral and rocky reefs. Often found in small groups swimming just above the reef. Ranges in depth from 2-25 m. Feeds on zooplankton.

Darkbar damsel (Weber's chromis) *Chromis weberi*

Attains 12 cm. A rather drab damselfish distinguished by its grey-green body and dark-edged scales. A prominent vertical black bar is present on the gill cover and a shorter bar follows the gill opening. The eye has a short vertical black line through it and the tail has black tips. Often seen swimming in groups above reefs in depths ranging from 10-40 m. Abundant in the Sodwana Bay and Aliwal Shoal areas. Diet consists of zooplankton.

Blacktail chromis *Chromis nigrura*

Attains 6 cm. This small damselfish has an overall bluish-grey colour with pale yellow flanks and a yellow tail with black margins. Several rows of blue spots occur along the body. An abundant damselfish found on shallow coral and rocky reefs between 1-30 m, ranging from the upper Eastern Cape coast northwards. Usually seen in small groups swimming just above the reef. Feeds on zooplankton.

Golden chromis (Ternate chromis) *Chromis ternatensis*

Attains 10 cm. The upper body colour is olive at the front and dark at the rear; the underside is pale with light blue centres to each scale, while the tail is clear with dark brown margins. An abundant damselfish, confined to coral reefs from Inhaca Island northwards; occurs in depths ranging from 2-30 m. Usually forms large feeding aggregations above branching corals where it feeds on zooplankton.

Bluespotted chromis

Blue puller

Chocolate dip

Darkbar damsel

Blacktail chromis

Golden chromis

Onespot damsel *Chrysiptera unimaculata*

Attains 8 cm. Juveniles have a yellowish body with a distinctive bright blue line extending from the forehead to the soft dorsal fin, terminating in a black spot. The colour of sub-adults changes to over-all brown with two yellow bars across body; adults are a uniform charcoal-grey colour. A common damselfish inhabiting rocky shores and tidal pools along the East Coast. Feeds mainly on algae.

Domino (Three-spot dascyllus) *Dascyllus trimaculatus*

Attains 14 cm. Has three white spots on a black body, resembling a domino. Large adults usually lose the white spots and turn an overall light charcoal-grey colour. A common damselfish, found in small groups on coral and rocky reefs at depths of 10-30 m. Juveniles often associate with large sea anemones, long spine sea urchins or small branching coral heads. Feeds primarily on zooplankton.

Zebra humbug (Humbug dascyllus) *Dascyllus aruanus*

Attains 8 cm. A distinctive species with a white body and three black bars. The front bar follows the shape of the head and the middle bar is angled backwards. An abundant inhabitant of coral reefs ranging from Maputaland northwards, although it has been recorded in the Durban area. A territorial fish that forms large groups around branching corals on sheltered reefs in depths of 1-20 m. When threatened they dart in unison for shelter amongst the coral branches. Feeds on zooplankton.

Black-tailed dascyllus *Dascyllus melanurus*

Attains 8 cm. This distinctive species is very similar to the zebra humbug (*D. aruanus*), except that the black bars are more vertical and there is a black area on the rear half of the caudal fin. Inhabits coral reefs in the Australasia region and not the Western Indian Ocean as previously thought. Territorial and often found with the more widespread zebra humbugs around branching corals in sheltered areas ranging in depth from 1-10 m. Less common than the zebra humbug. Feeds on zooplankton.

Twobar humbug (Indian dascyllus) *Dascyllus carneus*

Attains 7 cm. Body colour is whitish or pale tan with a vertical black bar at the pectoral fin base and a second black bar at the rear of body. The centre of the scales are marked with short blue lines on the body and head. The dorsal and anal fins are edged in blue. An abundant damselfish found on coral reefs north of Maputaland, only rarely seen on the deeper reefs at Sodwana Bay. Generally found in groups hovering above the shelter of branching coral heads at depths ranging from 5-35 m. Feeds on zooplankton.

Sash damsel *Plectroglyphidodon leucozonus*

Attains 12 cm. A widespread species, recognised by its overall brown colour and pale vertical bar across the mid-body. The bar fades with age. Juveniles have a black spot on the soft dorsal fin. Frequents exposed rocky shores and is common in tidal pools, especially in the Durban area. Guards its territory aggressively. Feeds primarily on algae.

Onespot damsel

Domino

Zebra humbug

Black-tailed dascyllus

Twobar humbug

Sash damsel

Blue pete (Caerulean damsel) *Pomacentrus caeruleus*

Attains 10 cm. One of the most striking East Coast damselfishes. Easily recognised by its brilliant blue body, yellow underside and yellow rear dorsal, pectoral, anal and tail fins. Ranges from southern KwaZulu-Natal northwards and inhabits both coral and rocky reefs in depths of 1-25 m. Occurs singly or in small groups, usually over rubble near the base of reefs. Feeds primarily on zooplankton.

Wrasses – Family Labridae

Wrasses are a large, diverse family of reef fishes that vary considerably in size. Most are small, elongate and have a continuous dorsal fin. The majority are beautifully coloured and some exhibit dramatic colour pattern changes with growth and between the sexes, which makes identification difficult. Sex change is common in this family. They have a distinct swimming style that depends more on the pectoral fins than the tail. All wrasses are carnivorous, but their food habits vary. Among the largest of the wrasses are those belonging to the genus *Bodianus*, which are commonly called hogfishes.

Goldsaddle hogfish *Bodianus perditio*

Attains 80 cm. The adult colour can be variable, but is generally reddish orange with small yellow spots on the head and a black saddle under the soft dorsal fin, preceded by a yellow or white bar. Juveniles are brownish yellow with a white crossbar preceding a large black blotch at the rear of the body. Not as common as other hogfishes, it occurs more frequently on coral reefs than on rocky reefs. Ranges in depth from 15-40 m. Found singly or in pairs and is known to undergo sex change. Preys on molluscs and crustaceans.

Turncoat hogfish (Axilspot hogfish) *Bodianus axillaris*

Attains 20 cm. Adults are dark reddish brown shading to white posteriorly; a black spot occurs at the base of the pectoral fin and on the soft dorsal and anal fins. Juveniles are black with eight white spots on each side of the body and tail. Rather uncommon, it inhabits both coral and rocky reefs at depths of 2-25 m with juveniles found in caves or under ledges. Juveniles feed on parasites and mucus which they pick off other fish. Adults prey on crustaceans.

Saddleback hogfish *Bodianus bilunulatus*

Attains 55 cm. This wrasse is basically reddish along the dorsal surface and sides, with a paler underside and a distinctive, large black saddle under the soft dorsal fin; this saddle disappears with age. Juveniles are different in colour and are yellow with a white underside and have a broad black band posteriorly. Common on both coral and rocky reefs and occurs at depths of 10-40 m. Usually found singly or in pairs. Preys primarily on molluscs and crustaceans.

Blue pete

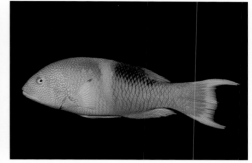

Goldsaddle hogfish

Turncoat hogfish (adult)

Turncoat hogfish (juvenile)

Saddleback hogfish (adult)

Saddleback hogfish (juvenile)

Diana's hogfish *Bodianus diana*

Attains 25 cm. This hogfish has a distinctive sloping forehead. Adults have a reddish to purplish-brown head, shading to dull yellow on flanks. The scales are edged in brown, and there are four yellow spots on the upper flanks. Juveniles are dark, reddish brown with rows of white blotches and small white spots on the body, and large black spots on the fins. A common inhabitant of coral and rocky reefs, ranging in depth from 6-80 m. Generally a solitary fish that spends much of the day actively foraging around the reef in search of food such as molluscs, crabs, sea urchins and corals.

Bluespotted tamarin (Bluespotted wrasse) *Anampses caeruleopunctatus*

Attains 30 cm. Females and juveniles are brownish orange overall with horizontal rows of small, dark-edged blue spots on body and fins, and dark-edged narrow blue bands on the head, some radiating from the eye. Adult males have an olive-green body with a vertical blue line on each scale; there is often a distinctive broad light green bar on the upper body behind the pectoral fin. Frequents coral and rocky reefs down to a depth of 40 m, but is more common on shallow coral reefs exposed to surge. An energetic swimmer that forages continuously for food during the daytime. Diet consists mainly of worms and small crustaceans. Found singly, in pairs or in small groups, usually with an adult male nearby. Buries itself in the sand at night for safety.

Clown coris (Clown wrasse) *Coris aygula*

Attains 70 cm. The juvenile of this large wrasse is most striking in appearance, being white overall with small black spots anteriorly, two large orange spots on the back, and a white-ringed black spot above each orange spot on the dorsal fin. Females have a whitish bar in front of the anal-fin origin; the body anterior to the bar is light yellowish green with small maroon spots, while the posterior is greenish with dark-edged scales, producing an overall dark green colouration. Adult males develop a large hump on the forehead and are deep blue-green, usually with one or two broad pale green bars in the centre of the body. An uncommon wrasse found on coral and rocky reefs down to a depth of at least 30 m. Juveniles are usually found near patches of sand or rubble and are occasionally seen in tidal pools. Buries itself in the sand at night or when threatened. Occurs singly and feeds on hard-shelled invertebrates such as crustaceans, sea urchins and molluscs.

Diana's hogfish (adult)

Diana's hogfish (juvenile)

Bluespotted tamarin (male)

Bluespotted tamarin (female)

Clown coris (adult)

Clown coris (juvenile)

Queen coris *Coris frerei*

Attains 60 cm. This uncommon wrasse has strikingly different colour phases. Females and young males are grey to dark grey-brown with small black spots on the sides of the body; the head is yellowish with a prominent light blue diagonal line extending down the head below the eye. Several other thin blue lines also occur on the head. Adult males are light brown with numerous small, light blue spots and closely spaced grey crossbars on the body, and pale green lines on the head. Juveniles are dark brownish orange with a broad black-edged white band crossing the body and dorsal fin just behind the gill cover. Two shorter white bands cross the head and two more appear on the rear of the body. Occurs on coral and rocky reefs at depths of 1-40 m and is usually found singly. Juveniles are some-times found in tidal pools and are popular with marine aquarists. Buries itself under the sand when threatened. Preys on crustaceans and molluscs.

African coris *Coris cuvieri*

Attains 35 cm. The juvenile is similar to the juvenile queen coris but the white bands on the back are shorter and the body is more orange than brown. Adults are brownish violet overall, with numer-ous small green spots on the body and caudal fin; light green lines occur on the head. The male has a light green vertical bar behind the pectoral fin. Buries itself under the sand when threatened. Juveniles are occasionally found in tidal pools and are popular with marine aquarists. Rather uncom-mon, it occurs on both coral and rocky reefs at depths of 1-50 m. Preys on molluscs and crustaceans.

Spottail coris *Coris caudimacula*

Attains 20 cm. This is the most common and abundant *coris* along the East Coast. The colour on the upper flanks is variable – usually green, pink or reddish brown with pale crossbars. The crossbars are absent on juveniles. Frequents rocky shores, coral and rocky reefs to depths of 30 m. Prefers sand and rubble areas near the reef. Usually seen swimming close to the bottom. Occurs singly and preys on crustaceans and molluscs.

Barred thicklip wrasse *Hemigymnus fasciatus*

Attains at least 40 cm. A rather uncommon wrasse, distinguished by very thick lips, a yellowish-green head with irregular blue-edged pink bands, and alternating broad black and narrow white crossbars on the body. The body colour of males reverses during courtship, as seen in the photograph. Undergoes various colour pattern changes from juvenile to adult. Inhabits mainly coral reefs at depths of 10-25 m. Generally a solitary fish. Preys on crustaceans and molluscs.

Queen coris (female adult)

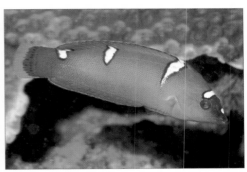

Queen coris (juvenile)

African coris (adult)

African coris (juvenile)

Spottail coris

Barred thicklip wrasse

Birdfish (Bird wrasse) *Gomphosus caeruleus*

Attains 28 cm. This wrasse has a characteristic elongated tubular snout with a terminal mouth, which makes identification easy. Females and young males are pale yellow, becoming darker on rear and upper body with a black spot on each scale except on the chest and lower belly. Adult males have an overall deep blue-green colour with pale yellowish-green margins to the dorsal and anal fins. This reasonably common wrasse inhabits both coral and rocky reefs at depths of 10-25 m and is found singly or in pairs. A very active swimmer that is constantly on the move over the reef in search of food. Its elongated snout is used to probe sand, rubble and crevices for small crustaceans. Occasionally small fish, brittle stars and molluscs are eaten.

Ringed wrasse (Longface or Pastel ringwrasse) *Hologymnosus doliatus*

Attains 38 cm. The colour pattern of this wrasse varies greatly between growth and sex phases. Adult males are pale blue-green with pinkish flanks and have closely spaced, thin lavender bars on the body; a broad pale yellowish band bordered by purple bars extends across the body midway between the pectoral fin base and anal fin origin. The head is blue-green with irregular yellowish to pink lines. Females and young males are greenish or pinkish grey with closely spaced orange-brown bars on the body. Juveniles are whitish with three narrow longitudinal orange-red stripes. Not a common wrasse, it inhabits coral and rocky reefs at depths of 12-30 m. Juveniles are often found in small groups swimming close to the bottom, while adults swim higher in the water above the reef. Diet consists mainly of small fish and occasionally crustaceans.

Rockmover wrasse *Novaculichthys taeniourus*

Attains 25 cm. Named for its habit of turning over small rocks in search of prey. Adults are dark brown with a vertical white line or spot on each scale. The belly is usually reddish, while the head is grey with irregular black lines radiating backwards from the eye. There is also a white bar at the base of the tail. Juveniles are mottled and banded green, reddish or brown and spotted with white. The first two rays of the dorsal fin are elongated. Juveniles are masters of camouflage and mimic drifting seaweed. This rather uncommon wrasse inhabits both coral and rocky reefs, ranging in depth from 2-20 m. Prefers areas of mixed sand and rubble. Preys upon invertebrate animals such as molluscs, crabs, sea urchins, worms and brittle stars. The adult is a difficult fish to approach; when cornered, it often hangs stationary in a near vertical position, attempting to blend in with the background.

Birdfish (male)

Birdfish (female)

Ringed wrasse (female)

Ringed wrasse (juvenile)

Rockmover wrasse (adult)

Rockmover wrasse (juvenile)

Bluestreak cleaner wrasse (Cleaner wrasse) *Labroides dimidiatus*

Attains 11 cm. A small, very elongate fish. The front half of its body is grey, while the rear is bright blue. A black horizontal band begins at the snout, widening towards the tail. Juveniles are overall bright blue with a black band along the body extending into the tail. Widely distributed, this common, lively fish ranges from rock pools to shallow coral and rocky reefs. Known as the 'doctor' of the reef, it feeds on parasites and mucus removed from 'clients' at established 'cleaning stations'. Occasionally seen entering larger fishes' mouths and gills to remove parasites. Sometimes occurs in small groups dominated by a single male. Sex change is common in this species.

Rainbow wrasse *Halichoeres iridis*

Attains 11 cm. Has distinctive dark red flanks and an orange head with green markings. Relatively uncommon, this small wrasse is found in depths greater than 20 m and inhabits mainly the flatter areas of coral and rocky reefs. Often occurs in pairs or threes, foraging for small invertebrates.

Checkerboard wrasse *Halichoeres hortulanus*

Attains 26 cm. A striking wrasse, aptly named. Adult males are blue-green with dark blue-edged scales, giving a checkered pattern. The head is green with pink bands, and there is a yellow blotch at the base of the dorsal fin. Females and young males are similar in appearance but have a whitish body and a black checkered pattern. Juveniles are broadly marked with large white and black areas on the body, and have a large, yellow-edged black spot on the dorsal fin. Commonly found on coral reefs at depths of 10-30 m. Occurs singly and swims rapidly around the reef, foraging for small invertebrates.

Adorned wrasse *Halichoeres cosmetus*

Attains 11 cm. A small, colourful wrasse with alternating narrow bluish-grey and yellow stripes along the body, and two black spots on the dorsal fin. Widespread along the East African coast. Reasonably common on coral and rocky reefs at depths of 10-30 m where it occurs singly. Juveniles prefer sandy areas around reefs, whilst adults frequent open rocky bottoms.

Goldbar wrasse *Thalassoma hebraicum*

Attains 25 cm. One of the most common East Coast wrasses. It has a distinctive vertical yellow bar just behind the pectoral fin. The body is greenish blue and the head brown-green with several prominent curved blue bands. Occurs on coral and rocky reefs to depths of 25 m, with juveniles often being found in tidal pools. Generally seen singly or in pairs. Males are strongly territorial, especially during the breeding season. An energetic wrasse which is constantly on the move, foraging for bottom-dwelling invertebrates.

Bluestreak cleaner wrasse

Rainbow wrasse

Checkerboard wrasse (adult)

Checkerboard wrasse (juvenile)

Adorned wrasse

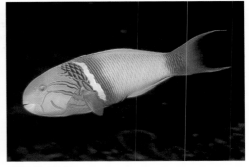

Goldbar wrasse

Twotone wrasse *Thalassoma amblycephalum*

Attains 16 cm. A small elongate wrasse. Females and young males have a broad blackish stripe from snout to tail; the upper body is greenish, whilst the underside is white. The tail margins have orange stripes. Adult males have a reddish body with closely spaced, vertical green lines, and a green head with a yellowish area behind it. This wrasse is common along rocky shores and on coral and rocky reefs to depths of 20 m and usually occur in small groups that swim energetically about the reef, feeding mainly on zooplankton.

Crescent-tail wrasse *Thalassoma lunare*

Attains 25 cm. An attractive wrasse; body is green with a vertical red line on each scale. The head is green with several irregular pink bands, and the caudal fin has a yellow centre. Relatively common on coral and rocky reefs at depths of 5-25 m. A bold, opportunistic fish, easily approached by divers. Occurs singly or in pairs. Actively swims about the reef foraging for bottom-dwelling invertebrates.

Ladder wrasse *Thalassoma trilobatum*

Attains 35 cm. Distinguished by its orange body and two ladder-like rows of blue-edged green stripes along the sides of the body. A common wrasse which frequents rocky shores and shallow reefs. Juveniles are often found in tidal pools. An active swimmer, constantly on the move. Adult males are territorial and usually have a harem. Feeds on crustaceans and molluscs.

Parrotfishes – Family Scaridae

Parrotfishes are close relatives of wrasses and are so named for their bright colours and their strong parrot-like beaks, which are used to scrape algae from rocks and to eat coral polyps. Adult males are generally different in colour to females and typically exhibit the brightest colours. During feeding large amounts of coral are taken in and ground in their gullets to extract organic food. Clouds of chalky residue are regularly excreted as these fishes move about the reef, making parrotfishes a major source of coral sand in tropical waters. At night some species secrete a protective cocoon of mucus around themselves while asleep in a suitable crevice. Sex change is common in this family.

Blue moon parrotfish (Black crescent parrotfish) *Scarus atrilunula*

Attains 30 cm. The adult male of this striking parrotfish is green overall with scales edged in pink, has pink cheeks and distinctive yellow margins to the caudal fin. Undergoes considerable colour change to reach the adult male phase. A rather uncommon parrotfish that frequents mainly coral reefs at depths of 10-30 m. Feeds on algae scraped from coral with its beak.

Blue humphead parrotfish (Saddled parrotfish) *Scarus cyanescens*

Attains 50 cm. A striking parrotfish with a distinct hump on the head. Body is dark blue with the posterior half bright green. This species was considered rare a few years ago but is now regularly seen on coral reefs, especially in the Sodwana Bay area. Ranges in depth from 10-30 m. Feeds on algae.

Twotone wrasse (male)

Twotone wrasse (female)

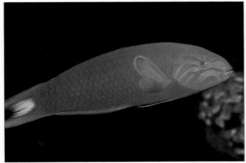

Crescent-tail wrasse

Ladder wrasse

Blue moon parrotfish (male)

Blue humphead parrotfish

Ember parrotfish (Redlip parrotfish) *Scarus rubroviolaceus*

Attains 65 cm. The adult male is overall bluish green while the front of the body is pinkish. Blue bands are present above and below the mouth. The female is red and has greenish upper flanks with irregular black stripes. Particularly abundant along the Maputaland coast, this common parrotfish is generally confined to coral reefs but is occasionally seen on rocky reefs as far south as the Protea Banks. Feeds on algae scraped from the reef with its beak.

Bluebarred parrotfish *Scarus ghobban*

Attains 75 cm. The female has a yellowish body with the centres of scales bluish, and five irregular blue bars across the body. The adult male is overall bluish green with scales rimmed in pale pink. It also has blue lines on the side of the head. One of the most widespread parrotfishes; inhabits shallow reefs and adjacent sandy areas, lagoons and bays. Usually solitary and feeds on algae.

Mullets — Family Mugilidae

Flathead mullet *Mugil cephalus*

Attains 60 cm. Mullets are recognised by their silvery, elongated bodies, large scales and double dorsal fin. Due to the similarity between species it is not easy to distinguish between them without close examination. The flathead mullet is recognised by a blunt snout and diffused horizontal stripes on its flanks. These shoaling fishes frequent shallow coastal and estuarine waters. They are bottom-feeders and pick up mouthfuls of mud to strain out suitable food. Algae is also included in their diet.

Sandsmelts — Family Mugiloididae

Sandsmelts, or sandperches as they are known in some regions, are a group of small, elongate, cylindrical fishes with large mouths and thick lips that live in sand and rubble areas near reefs. They rest on the bottom, propping themselves on their pelvic fins, ready to ambush prey. When threatened, they dash off and then come to an abrupt halt. Their eyes are pronounced and oriented as much upwards as laterally. Can be confused with lizardfishes, but have a longer, more pointed mouth, long, continuous dorsal and anal fins, and a square tail. They are territorial and generally easily approached underwater.

Spotted sandsmelt *Parapercis punctulata*

Attains 15 cm. Recognised by its silvery-white body, a line of dark red blotches on lower body, small dark spots on back, and the conspicuous black spinous portion of the dorsal fin. The male has two dark lines across the belly and the female three black spots on either side of the belly. One of the most common sandsmelts, found on coral reefs, but only occasionally seen on rocky reefs. Ranges in depth from 10-30 m and occurs singly or in pairs. Feeds on crabs, shrimps and, occasionally, small fish.

Blacktail sandsmelt (Speckled sandsmelt) *Parapercis hexophtalma*

Attains 26 cm. Has a distinctive large black blotch in the centre of the tail. The upper body is pale greenish brown, speckled with brown spots, and the lower body is white with rows of black spots. A common shallow-water species, generally confined to protected coral reefs where it inhabits sand and rubble areas. It has, however, been recorded as far south as the Durban area. Usually occurs singly. Feeds on crabs and shrimps and, occasionally, small fish.

Ember parrotfish (male)

Ember parrotfish (female)

Bluebarred parrotfish (female)

Flathead mullet

Spotted sandsmelt

Blacktail sandsmelt

Smallscale sandsmelt *Parapercis robinsoni*

Attains 30 cm. The body is whitish and has dark brown-green mottling on the back and nine black bars ventrally. Several bluish lines are present on the head. Inhabits coral and rocky reefs at depths of 10-30 m. Common in the Aliwal Shoal area. Preys on small invertebrates and fish.

Blennies – Family Blenniidae

Blennies are a prolific family of small fishes that live mainly in shallow waters and in the intertidal zone; they are generally bottom living. These inconspicuous fishes are mostly elongated, have a continuous dorsal fin, large pelvic fins and a blunt head with high-set, protruding eyes. Many have tentacles or a fleshy crest on the upper part of the head. Because of their small size and ability to change colours and markings to blend with the background, blennies often go unnoticed. Similar to gobies in appearance and habits but tend to curve and flex their bodies while resting or swimming, in contrast to gobies who hold their bodies still and straight. Most species feed on algae by scraping with specially adapted teeth.

Leopard rockskipper *Exellias brevis*

Attains 12 cm. Recognised by its deep, whitish body covered with numerous small, dark spots. Confined to coral reefs, this relatively uncommon blenny is found among the branches of *Acropora* corals. It tends to mimic the coral in which it lives in an effort to disguise itself. Occurs at depths of 10-30 m. Diet consists of algae and coral polyps.

Streaky rockskipper *Istiblennius dussumieri*

Attains 10 cm. This blenny is distinguished by the dusky vertical bands along its tan-coloured body and branched eye-tentacles. A common, widely distributed inhabitant of tidal pools, often occurring in small groups. Feeds on algae.

Bandit blenny *Omobranchus banditus*

Attains 6 cm. Has distinctive, alternating dark brown and light brown bands on the body and head. Ranges from central Mozambique southwards to the Eastern Cape. Reasonably common, it inhabits rocky shores and tidal pools. Feeds on algae and crustaceans.

Horned rockskipper *Antennablennius bifilum*

Attains 15 cm. An attractive blenny with a mottled appearance, and about seven dark bands and many small white spots along the flanks. Colour can vary, depending on sex. Ranges from Namibia to Sodwana Bay and is a common tidal pool inhabitant. Feeds on algae and crustaceans.

Ringneck blenny *Parablennius pilicornis*

Attains 12 cm. A rather inconspicuous blenny, with up to nine vertical dark brown bars that separate into brown spots ventrally. Has branched eye-tentacles and orange spots on the head. An endemic and abundant fish that ranges from the southern Cape to Sodwana Bay. Occurs in tidal pools and on offshore reefs and shipwrecks. Feeds on algae and crustaceans.

Smallscale sandsmelt

Leopard rockskipper

Streaky rockskipper

Bandit blenny

Horned rockskipper

Ringneck blenny

Twostripe blenny (Sabretooth blenny, Bluestriped fangblenny) *Plagiotremus rhinorhynchos*

Attains 9 cm. Two distinct colour phases can occur with this small, slender fish. Either blue with a black stripe from snout to tail, or orange with two narrow blue lines from snout to tail. Unlike most blennies, which tend to be bottom-dwellers, this one is free-swimming. Fairly common on shallow coral and rocky reefs, it usually occurs singly or in pairs and does not stray far from the reef. Mimics the cleaner wrasse (see page 80) by pretending to remove parasites and mucus off other fish, but instead feeds off them by taking bites out of their scales or flesh and then beating a hasty retreat.

Piano blenny (Scale-eating fangblenny) *Plagiotremus tapeinosoma*

Attains 12 cm. This small, slender fish has a yellowish upper body overlaid with a black stripe broken into many segments, hence its common name. The underside is pink and white. A striking blenny, similar in distribution and habitat to the twostripe blenny (see above). Feeds on the scales and flesh of other fish as its source of food. Known to nibble at the bare legs and arms of divers.

Triplefins – Family Tripterygiidae

Hotlips triplefin *Helcogramma obtusirostre*

Attains 4,5 cm. Triplefins are similar to blennies but are placed in their own family. They typically feature three separate dorsal fins and a rather pointed mouth. Males are more colourful than females. These very small bottom-dwelling fish are well camouflaged and are only noticed when they dart from one position to another. The hotlips triplefin is abundant in the intertidal zone along the KwaZulu-Natal coast. Feeds on algae and tiny invertebrates.

Gobies – Family Gobiidae

Gobies constitute the largest single family of marine fish. Most are small and inconspicuous and so are seldom seen. Only a few of the more common species are included here. Gobies and blennies are often mistaken for each other but can be distinguished by their dorsal fins. Gobies have two, while blennies have one long, continuous fin. Another difference is the tendency of gobies to rest in a stiff, straight position, while blennies are more flexed and curved. Generally bottom living but a few hover just above the reef. The bottom-living species rest on their pectoral and pelvic fins. In surge or current, a small suction disc is formed between the pelvic fins to anchor themselves in place. They range from reefs to rocky shores, estuaries and mangrove swamps. Feeding habits vary according to species.

Whitespotted goby *Bathygobius coalitus*

Attains 12 cm. Has a brownish body with elongated dark blotches and white spots forming longitudinal rows. A fairly common, bottom-dwelling goby that inhabits tidal pools and rocky shores. Ranges from Inhaca Island to the Eastern Cape. Diet consists of small bottom-dwelling invertebrates.

Firegoby (Fire dartfish) *Nemateleotris magnifica*

Attains 9 cm. One of the prettiest and most graceful of gobies. The front part of the body is greyish, the rear part red, and the caudal fin dark red. Has a distinctive long yellow first dorsal fin. A shy and timid free-swimming goby which generally inhabits coral and rocky reefs in depths of 15-50 m where it occurs singly, in pairs or in small groups. Hovers above its burrow in the sand or rock and inevitably makes a hasty retreat when approached. Tends to flick its long yellow dorsal spine when it feels threatened. Feeds on zooplankton.

Scissortail (Concord, Blackfin dartfish) *Ptereleotris evides*

Attains 12 cm. Rather uncommon, this elegant free-swimming goby is light bluish grey, shading posteriorly to dark blue. Inhabits both coral and rocky reefs and is found as far south as the Aliwal Shoal area, ranging in depth from 12-30 m. Adults generally swim in pairs and juveniles form small groups. One of the most difficult fish to approach closely as it keeps its distance or darts back into its burrow if it feels threatened. Feeds on zooplankton.

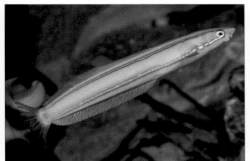

Twostripe blenny

Piano blenny

Hotlips triplefin

Whitespotted goby

Firegoby

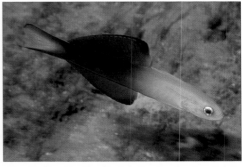

Scissortail

Pennant glider (Golden headed jawfish, Blue-streak goby) *Valenciennea strigata*

Attains 18 cm. A small elongated fish with a light grey body and a distinctive black-edged blue stripe below the eye. The lower half of the head is yellow and the first dorsal has extended spiny rays. A fairly common goby found on sandy bottoms with loose rocks near the edge of reefs. Ranges in depth from 10-25 m. Often seen in pairs hovering near their burrows. It has a characteristic habit of constantly digging sand and sifting it through its gills for food particles. Tends to dart back into its burrow when approached.

Surgeonfishes – Family Acanthuridae

Surgeonfishes are some of the most exquisitely patterned and coloured reef fishes. They are generally small to medium sized, oval in shape, thin-bodied and have high-set eyes and a small mouth. They all feature one or two pairs of erectable scalpel-like spines that fold forward into a groove (sheath) on either side of the base of their tail when not in use. These give the family its common name. The spines are used during inter-territorial disputes and in defence. Surgeonfishes are a very important group of herbivores as they help control the growth of algae on reefs, which would otherwise restrict animal resettlement. Some deep-water shoaling species feed on zooplankton. Fishes of the genus *Zebrasoma* are referred to as tangs. Unicornfishes are a sub-family of surgeonfishes. They have a more elongate body and some develop a horn-like protrusion on the forehead.

Pencilled surgeon (Eyestripe surgeonfish) *Acanthurus dussumieri*

Attains 54 cm. The main distinguishing features of this fish are the white tail spine sheath and a blue tail with numerous black spots, changing to yellow at the base. The body is brown with closely spaced thin wavy blue horizontal lines, and the anal fin has a bright blue margin. A common surgeonfish, found on coral and rocky reefs in depths of 2-25 m. Feeds on algae.

Powder-blue surgeonfish *Acanthurus leucosteron*

Attains 23 cm. This strikingly colourful surgeonfish is unmistakable, with its bright blue body, black and white head, yellow dorsal fin and white anal and pelvic fins. Common on shallow coral and rocky reefs to depths of 15 m. Juveniles are occasionally seen along rocky shores. Found singly or in small groups grazing on the reef for algae. Sometimes forms large shoals in tropical areas.

Bluebanded surgeon (Clown surgeon, Striped surgeonfish) *Acanthurus lineatus*

Attains 38 cm. A striking surgeonfish with horizontal black-edged blue stripes interspersed with yellow, and a purple underside. Frequents the shallower, more turbulent areas of rocky reefs where it is reasonably common. Sometimes ventures to deeper reefs in search of food. An energetic fish; moves rapidly about its territory on reef. Juveniles occasionally found in tidal pools. Feeds on algae.

Brown surgeon (Dusky surgeonfish) *Acanthurus nigrofuscus*

Attains 20 cm. This rather inconspicuous fish has a drab brown colour and small orange spots on the head which are not very noticeable. Common in tidal pools and on shallow coral and rocky reefs. Occurs either singly or in small groups, and feeds on filamentous algae.

Elongate surgeon *Acanthurus mata*

Attains 50 cm. A large surgeonfish, often observed swimming in shoals over deep reefs. Overall yellowish brown with longitudinal thin blue lines on head and body; has yellow marking around the eye. This surgeonfish is able to change its body colour from dark bluish brown to light slaty blue, depending on its behavioural mood. Relatively common on coral and rocky reefs to depths of at least 40 m. Feeds on zooplankton in mid-water.

Pennant glider

Pencilled surgeon

Powder-blue surgeonfish

Bluebanded surgeon

Brown surgeon

Elongate surgeon

Lieutenant surgeonfish *Acanthurus tennenti*

Attains 31 cm. General body colour can vary from greyish brown to dark brown, depending on behavioural mood. The bright blue edging to fins and tail spine, and the two black marks in the shoulder region are very noticeable. Found on coral and rocky reefs; particularly common in the Sodwana Bay area. Generally observed singly or in pairs and occurs in depths of 10-25 m. Feeds on algae.

Convict surgeon (Banded surgeon) *Acanthurus triostegus*

Attains 27 cm. Recognised by the six vertical black bars on a grey-green body, shading to white on the underside. One of the most common surgeonfishes along the East Coast. Confined to shallow inshore reefs and tidal pools. Often seen in large shoals grazing algae on rocks.

Twospot bristletooth *Ctenochaetus binotatus*

Attains 26 cm. The colour of this rather dull surgeonfish is orangish brown to dark brown, with numerous thin blue longitudinal lines on the body; the head is covered with small blue dots, and the iris of the eye is blue. Neither the lines nor the spots are very noticeable. A common surgeonfish, found on coral and rocky reefs ranging in depth from 12-50 m. Feeds on detritus and soft algae.

Spotted bristletooth (Goldring bristletooth) *Ctenochaetus strigosus*

Attains 18 cm. This species features a conspicuous yellow eye ring. The body is yellowish brown with numerous inconspicuous, thin, bluish-grey longitudinal lines which sometimes appear as dots. The head is covered with yellow or bluish dots. Uncommon, it ranges from Maputaland northwards and occurs mainly on coral reefs in depths of 2-40 m. Feeds on soft algae.

Sailfin tang *Zebrasoma veliferum*

Attains 40 cm. This majestic member of the surgeonfish family has well-developed, sail-like dorsal and anal fins, particularly in the case of juveniles, hence the descriptive name. Juveniles have yellow fins with alternating vertical yellow and dark brown bars on body. Adults have alternating broad dark brown and narrow whitish bars, with additional narrow yellow lines on the bars. Small yellow spots are present on the head and belly. Generally confined to coral reefs. Juveniles tend to shelter amongst the branches of *Acropora* corals. Feeds on plankton and soft algae.

Lieutenant surgeonfish

Convict surgeon

Twospot bristletooth

Spotted bristletooth

Sailfin tang (adult)

Sailfin tang (juvenile)

Twotone tang (Brushtail tang) *Zebrasoma scopas*

Attains 20 cm. The juvenile phase of this tang is particulary handsome. Closely related to the sailfin tang, it has well-developed, sail-like dorsal and anal fins, especially as juveniles. Adults are dark yellowish brown with tiny pale blue dots on head and body, with those on the body tending to join to form longitudinal lines. Juveniles have pale vertical lines on the body. Both phases have a distinctive white sheath to the caudal spine. This uncommon tang is found singly or in pairs and is confined to coral reefs at depths of 1-60 m. Juveniles are often observed near the branches of *Acropora* corals, which are used as a refuge when danger approaches. Feeds on algae.

Orange-spine unicorn *Naso lituratus*

Attains 45 cm. Unicornfishes are a sub-family of surgeonfishes. They are generally characterised by an obvious protrusion on the forehead, but not all unicornfishes have this. The orange-spine unicorn, which lacks a protrusion on the forehead, is the most strikingly coloured of the family and is distinguished by its angular head, dark brown body with facial 'make-up' of black and yellowish-orange markings, yellow dorsal fin with a blue margin, and two prominent yellowish-orange knife-like keel plates at the base of the tail. Males develop long, filamentous tail lobes. Generally inhabits coral reefs but occasionally reaches the Aliwal Shoal area. Occurs singly or in pairs and feeds on leafy algae.

Moorish Idol – Family Zanclidae

Moorish idol *Zanclus canescens*

Attains 22 cm. This single member of the family is a close relative of the surgeonfishes (see page 90). Often confused with the coachman (see page 60) as it also has a long white dorsal filament, but can be distinguished by its longer, protruding mouth, the black, white and yellow crossbars on the body, and its black and white tail. Common on shallow coral reefs and rocky reefs as far south as the Eastern Cape. Its protruding mouth is used to feed on algae and small invertebrates living in crevices.

Rabbitfishes – Family Siganidae

Whitespotted rabbitfish *Siganus sutor*

Attains 45 cm. Rabbitfishes have a compressed, oval-shaped body, a small mouth and venomous fin spines. They occur in shoals around estuarine flats and in smaller numbers on shallow coral and rocky reefs. The whitespotted rabbitfish has a greyish body with sparsely spaced blue spots on its flanks. The dorsal fin and upper portion of the head are pale yellow. Capable of varying its colour pattern, depending on its mood and the colour of the substrate. Feeds mainly on seaweed and grasses.

Triggerfishes – Family Balistidae

Triggerfishes are robust fish with compressed, oval-shaped bodies and high-set eyes. The first dorsal spine can be locked in an erect position by the second trigger-like spine. They swim by undulations of the soft dorsal and anal fins, bringing the tail into action only when speed is needed. When threatened, they usually seek refuge in a hole or crevice in the reef, firmly wedging themselves by erecting the dorsal spine. Triggerfishes have strong beak-like teeth which are used for crushing shellfish, crustaceans and sea urchins. Some species are omnivorous, others are plankton feeders.

Clown triggerfish (Waistcoat triggerfish) *Balistoides conspicillum*

Attains 50 cm. The most striking of the family, with its bright orange snout, black body and white-spotted belly. Widespread, but only relatively common, it inhabits shallow coral and rocky reefs from the Protea Banks northwards. A rather shy, solitary fish that is usually difficult to approach. Tends to be territorial. Preys on crustaceans, shellfish and sea urchins.

Twotone tang (adult)

Twotone tang (juvenile)

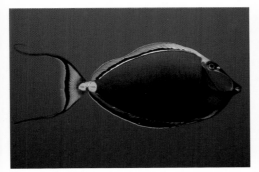
Orange-spine unicorn

Moorish idol

Whitespotted rabbitfish

Clown triggerfish

Redfang triggerfish (Blue triggerfish) *Odonus niger*

Attains 50 cm. This common triggerfish has a distinctive deep body with a jutting lower jaw and an overall dark blue colour. Often occurs in large groups which congregate in mid-water above coral and rocky reefs. Feeds mainly on zooplankton in mid-water. When approached it frequently dives into a hole or crevice in the reef. Can be aggressive to divers during spawning.

Boomerang triggerfish *Sufflamen bursa*

Attains 25 cm. A small, solitary triggerfish, distinguished by its greyish-brown body, whitish belly and two distinctive yellow curved lines from pectoral fin base to first dorsal fin. These lines can change to brown, depending on behavioural mood. Relatively common, it inhabits shallow coral and rocky reefs as far south as the Protea Banks. Feeds on algae, molluscs and crustaceans.

Halfmoon triggerfish *Sufflamen chrysopterus*

Attains 30 cm. A widespread and common triggerfish, identified by its dark brown body, purplish-blue belly, a distinctive vertical yellow line behind the eye, and a white-edged yellowish-brown tail. Capable of altering its overall colour to light yellowish brown. A solitary fish found on coral and rocky reefs ranging in depth from 10-30 m. When approached, it invariably darts into a crevice. Feeds on crustaceans, molluscs and sea urchins.

Bridle triggerfish *Sufflamen fraenatus*

Attains 38 cm. Less colourful than most other triggerfishes, the bridle triggerfish has an overall light brown body. Males have pinkish-yellow markings around the mouth, forming a 'bridle' pattern, a feature juveniles and females lack. A common, solitary triggerfish, found on coral and rocky reefs along the East Coast at depths of 10-30 m. Preys on sea urchins, crustaceans and molluscs.

Blackbar triggerfish (Picasso triggerfish) *Rhinecanthus aculeatus*

Attains 25 cm. One of the most striking triggerfishes. The main colour features are a number of diagonal bluish-white bars on the rear of the lower body, a distinctive yellow 'bridle' pattern extending from the mouth and a blue and yellow-brown stripe across the head passing through the eye. Ranges from Maputaland northwards where it inhabits shallow reefs, lagoons and sheltered shores. Abundant in sandy areas with rubble. Mostly solitary and tends to dart into a crevice or hole when approached. Feeds on a wide variety of invertebrates, molluscs and algae.

Filefishes – Family Monacanthidae

Honeycomb filefish (Wire-net filefish) *Cantherhines pardalis*

Attains 20 cm. Filefishes, or leatherjackets as they are also known, are closely related to triggerfishes (see page 94), but have more compressed bodies, generally a more pointed snout, and a longer first dorsal spine. The scales are smaller and coarse, giving the skin a file-like texture. Most species are able to change their colour to match their surroundings. The honeycomb filefish has pale green to greyish-blue reticulations on the sides, producing a honeycomb appearance. Ranges from the Eastern Cape northwards. A solitary and secretive fish, found on coral and rocky reefs ranging in depth from 2-20 m. Feeds on a variety of invertebrates.

Redfang triggerfish

Boomerang triggerfish

Halfmoon triggerfish

Bridle triggerfish

Blackbar triggerfish

Honeycomb filefish

Boxfishes — Family Ostraciidae

Boxfishes are close relatives of blaasops and porcupinefishes and are so named because the head and body are encased in a protective skeletal armour-plated box. They lack pelvic fins, have a small mouth and are usually brightly coloured and patterned. The patterns often vary with age and sex. A rather sluggish reef fish, but surprisingly manoeuvrable. Boxfishes are able to secrete a poisonous mucus from their skin to protect them from predators.

Whitespotted boxfish *Ostracion meleagris*

Attains 25 cm. The male and the female of this boxfish are distinctly different in colour. Females and juveniles are black with numerous small white spots; males are dark brown on top with white spots, and the lower flanks are violet with yellow spots. A yellow line separates the change in the upper and lower markings. This reasonably common boxfish inhabits rocky shores and coral and rocky reefs ranging in depth from 1-30 m. Feeds on algae, sponges and invertebrates.

Boxy *Ostracion cubicus*

Attains 45 cm. Juveniles of this striking fish have a bright yellow, cube-shaped body with small black spots; adults develop a more elongated body and are yellowy green with black-edged blue spots. A fairly common boxfish that inhabits rocky shores and coral and rocky reefs that range in depth from 1-30 m. Feeds on algae, sponges and invertebrates.

Blaasops — Family Tetraodontidae

Blaasops, or puffers, as they are more commonly known, are divided into two groups; the Tetraodontinae and the Canthigasterinae; the latter group is known as sharpnose puffers, or tobies, and consists of small, often colourful fish. They all have the ability, when threatened, to inflate themselves by swallowing water, making it difficult for a predator to swallow them. As an additional protection, the skin and some internal organs contain a deadly poison. Blaasops have a scaleless skin, lack pelvic fins and have fused teeth that form a beak which is used to crush crabs, molluscs and sea urchins. They swim about the reef in a slow, almost clumsy manner.

Guineafowl blaasop *Arothron meleagris*

Attains 35 cm. Distinguished by its brown-grey body densely covered with small white spots. Relatively uncommon, it mainly inhabits coral reefs but has been recorded as far south as Durban. Occurs at depths of 3-20 m; usually solitary. Feeds on the tips of branching corals, algae and invertebrates.

Blackspotted blaasop *Arothron nigropunctatus*

Attains 30 cm. Exhibits a great deal of colour variety, from grey to brown to bright yellow, but always has widely scattered black spots of varying size on the body. Fairly common, it occurs on coral and rocky reefs at depths of 10-25 m. Feeds on algae, sponges and sea squirts.

Star blaasop (Star puffer) *Arothron stellatus*

Attains 90 cm. The largest of the blaasop family. Adults are whitish with small black spots on the head, body and fins. Juveniles are orange with small black spots on the upper body and irregular, broad, diagonal black bands on the belly. With age, the orange fades and the diagonal bands turn to spots. Rather uncommon, it occurs on coral and rocky reefs and occasionally shipwrecks, ranging in depth from 5-58 m. Usually seen singly or in pairs. Feeds on sponges, corals and hard-shelled invertebrates.

Whitespotted boxfish (male)

Whitespotted boxfish (female/juvenile)

Boxy

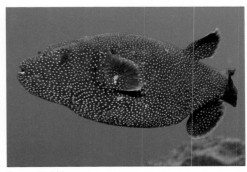

Guineafowl blaasop

Blackspotted blaasop

Star blaasop

Whitespotted blaasop (Whitespotted puffer) *Arothron hispidus*

Attains 48 cm. Distinguished by its greyish to greenish-brown upper body, shading to white below with curved dark stripes and small white spots on upper body and tail. Just behind the gill cover and at the base of the pectoral fins, there is a dark patch surrounded by a circular yellow pattern. This reasonably common blaasop ranges from the Eastern Cape northwards and inhabits coral and rocky reefs at depths of 1-50 m. Juveniles are common in the weedy areas of estuaries. Feeds on a wide variety of plants and animals, including the crown-of-thorns starfish.

Spotted toby (Ambon toby) *Canthigaster amboinensis*

Attains 15 cm. This small pufferfish is widespread and relatively common. Recognised by its brown body covered with numerous small white spots, and blue lines on its head. With age, the white spots change to light blue and additional black spots develop. The head is more angular than in most other pufferfishes. Frequents sheltered rocky shores and coral and rocky reefs, at depths ranging from 1-20 m. A fast swimmer when threatened. Feeds on bottom-living invertebrates.

Bi-coloured toby (Puffer) *Canthigaster smithae*

Attains 13 cm. An attractive pufferfish, featuring white sides covered with tiny blue spots, a dark brown back, a yellow stripe from head to tail on the lower side of the body, and a shorter stripe along the upper back. The yellow area around the eye has radiating blue lines resembling eyelashes. Occurs on both coral and rocky reefs in depths of 15-40 m. Uncommon in southern African waters but common in tropical areas. Feeds on algae and a variety of shelled invertebrates.

Model toby (Black-saddled toby) *Canthigaster valentini*

Attains 11 cm. This attractive pufferfish is a favourite with marine aquarists. It has four saddle-shaped dark areas on the upper body, a creamy lower body covered with brown spots, and a yellow tail. Reasonably common, it is found in areas such as harbours, piers, sheltered rocky shores and on coral and rocky reefs in depths ranging from 1-20 m. Feeds on algae and bottom-living invertebrates.

Porcupinefishes – Family Diodontidae

Shortspine porcupinefish (Black blotched porcupinefish) *Diodon liturosus*

Attains 50 cm. Porcupinefishes have similar features to blaasops but are distinguished by the spines on their scales. The spines are normally held flat, but when threatened the fish can inflate itself into a spiky ball twice its normal size to deter predators. The shortspine porcupinefish is recognised by its brown body, pale underside and the irregular white-edged black markings on the upper body. A widespread and fairly common species, inhabiting coral and rocky reefs at depths of 10-25 m. Feeds primarily on hard-shelled invertebrates.

Whitespotted blaasop

Spotted toby

Bi-coloured toby

Model toby

Shortspine porcupinefish

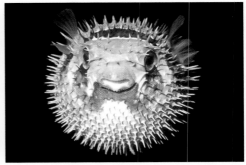

Shortspine porcupinefish (inflated)

CORALS

INTRODUCTION

Corals (Phylum Cnidaria) are distributed in many oceans and seas and are particularly abundant in tropical and sub-tropical regions, where they exhibit a great variety of size, form, texture and colour. The coral structure is made up of tiny carnivorous animals known as polyps which belong to the large group, or phylum, of invertebrate animals called Cnidaria. These include animals such as jellyfish, anemones, and hydroids.

Coral polyps are generally sessile, that is, fixed or attached to the reef. The coral polyp can be likened to an anemone, the body consisting of a tube of soft tissue, closed at the bottom and open at the top. The stomach cavity forming the centre of the body has a mouth but no anus. To increase the surface area for the absorbtion of food, the stomach cavity is partitioned by radiating strips of tissue called mesenteries. The mouth is ringed by tentacles armed with stinging cells which are used for seizing and paralysing prey, and for warding off potential predators.

Generally, polyps form colonies which are united by extensions of their tissues, enabling them to share nutrition. The polyps can extend their tentacles when feeding and can withdraw them into the safety of the skeleton. The primary diet of coral polyps is zooplankton, which is supplemented in most corals with nutrients produced by single-celled symbiotic algae called zooxanthellae, living within the tissues of the polyps. Zooxanthellae, using the sun's energy, produce nutrition for themselves and provide materials which enhance the coral's ability to form a skeleton. This dependency on sunlight restricts the depth at which some corals can live. Corals that do not contain zooxanthellae are not restricted in depth and can live in very deep water. The coral's colour is produced both by its own pigments and by the various colours and concentrations of zooxanthellae living in its tissues.

Corals enlarge their colony by asexual budding, or dividing, of existing polyps, but can also reproduce sexually from eggs and sperm; these develop into free-swimming larvae that settle and attach themselves to a reef to form a new colony. For most corals to thrive they need shallow warm water, usually at temperatures above 23°C. Individual corals can live in colder waters, but they do not form extensive reefs. Other requirements are clear water, long hours of sunshine for zooxanthellae to flourish, and water that is relatively sediment-free.

The identification of different coral species is dependent on the skeletal features, and often requires close examination by a coral expert. In this book, therefore, where doubt exists as to the exact species, only the coral genus (group with similar characteristics) is given. The descriptive or common names adopted are 'umbrella' names used to describe the various species within a particular genus or, in the case of *Acropora*, the various growth forms.

COMMON CORAL TYPES

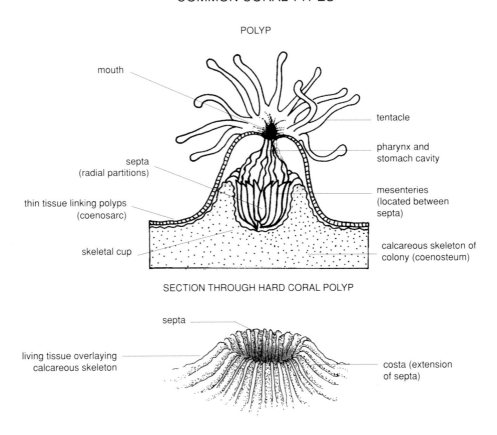

POLYP

mouth

tentacle

pharynx and
stomach cavity

septa
(radial partitions)

mesenteries
(located between
septa)

thin tissue linking polyps
(coenosarc)

skeletal cup

calcareous skeleton of
colony (coenosteum)

SECTION THROUGH HARD CORAL POLYP

septa

living tissue overlaying
calcareous skeleton

costa (extension
of septa)

HARD CORAL CORALLITE (polyp retracted)

Hard Corals
(Order Scleractinia)

Hard corals are the primary animals responsible for the formation of coral reefs. The anemone-like polyps of hard corals generally form colonies and live within a communal skeleton. The polyps secrete calcium carbonate (limestone) which forms a hard stony skeletal cup, known as a corallite, to support and protect their soft body. Usually the wall of the corallite is reinforced by a number of thin vertical radial limestone partitions, called septa. The upper edges of these septa are free at the top of the corallite and, in many species, extend outside the cup as lines or ridges, forming distinctive patterns. Polyps usually have tentacles in multiples of six, and their bodies are connected to their neighbours' by means of a thin layer of fleshy tissue which covers the skeleton. Polyps grow by extending the wall of their corallite upwards. During the day, most hard coral polyps are withdrawn into the safety of their corallites. Feeding generally takes place at night, when zooplankton is most abundant. Hard corals occur in an infinite variety of forms such as branches, plates, domes, encrusting sheets and leaves. Variations in growth form and even colour can occur within the same species, depending on the environmental conditions in which they live.

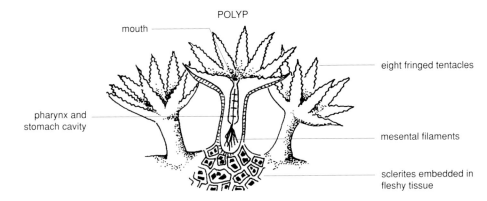

POLYP

mouth

eight fringed tentacles

pharynx and
stomach cavity

mesental filaments

sclerites embedded in
fleshy tissue

Soft Corals
(Order Alcyonacea: Octocorals)

Although involved only to a limited extent in reef-building, soft corals form an integral part of a coral reef. Unlike hard corals, soft corals do not secrete an outer skeleton but have an internal one consisting of numerous small calcareous (limestone) particles called sclerites embedded in the coral's fleshy tissue. These give the body support but allow it to remain soft and flexible. Colonies are made up of a

large number of identical polyps connected by the fleshy tissue. Each polyp has eight feathery tentacles which are concealed within the fleshy body when retracted. Most soft corals contain symbiotic zooxanthellae, to which they owe their green and brown colourations. Others are more brilliantly coloured due to pigments incorporated in their sclerites. They also produce toxic substances which are distasteful to most predators and which are used to deter hard corals when competing for space on the reef. Some soft corals feed only at night, others during the day.

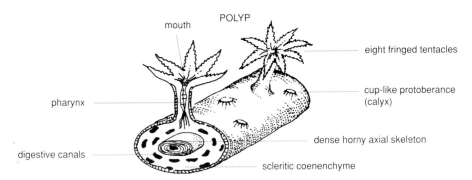

POLYP

mouth

eight fringed tentacles

cup-like protoberance
(calyx)

pharynx

dense horny axial skeleton

digestive canals

scleritic coenenchyme

Gorgonian Corals
(Order Gorgonacea: Octocorals)

These include sea fans and sea whips. The axial skeletons of these plant-like colonies are made of a tough but flexible horny material called gorgonin, or of calcium carbonate, or both. The polyps are housed in tiny cup-like protuberances, scattered over the branches, and are joined together by a fleshy layer called coenenchyme, which is usually impregnated with sclerites. When extended, the

polyps appear as tiny white flowers with eight feathery tentacles. Food is shared between polyps via small canals which interconnect the stomachs of neighbouring polyps.

Shallow-water gorgonians contain zooxanthellae, while deep-water ones do not. Gorgonians which have a horny skeleton are very flexible and can bend with the current, whereas those with a calcium carbonate skeleton are less flexible, and therefore they inhabit areas that are protected from the current, such as caves, crevices or deep water.

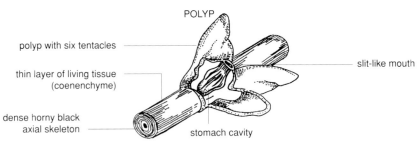

POLYP

polyp with six tentacles

thin layer of living tissue
(coenenchyme)

dense horny black
axial skeleton

slit-like mouth

stomach cavity

Black Corals
(Order Antipatharia)

Black corals form unbranched or branched plant-like colonies resembling trees, ferns, plumes and whips. Colonies may grow to several metres in height. Its skeleton is made of a very flexible, dense, horny material, similar to that of gorgonians, which is dark brown or black in colour, hence the coral's common name. The polyps usually bear six simple tentacles, have slit-like mouths and are housed in cup-like protuberances spread over the colony. Unlike those of gorgonian corals, the polyps of black corals cannot be fully withdrawn. The skeleton is covered with a thin delicate layer of pale coloured living tissue which connects the polyps, enabling the colony to share food. Black corals do not contain zooxanthellae and are therefore not dependent on sunlight and can live in deep water. In some countries they are collected, cut and polished to make jewellery.

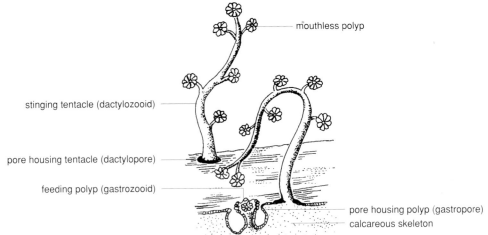

mouthless polyp

stinging tentacle (dactylozooid)

pore housing tentacle (dactylopore)

feeding polyp (gastrozooid)

pore housing polyp (gastropore)

calcareous skeleton

Hydroid Corals
(Order Milleporina)

The members of this order belong to the class Hydrozoa, a large varied group that includes animals such as the blue-bottle. A few coral-like animals belong to this class but are only remotely related to true (scleractinian) corals. One such group is fire corals, which superficially resemble true corals, and also lay down calcareous (limestone) skeletons. They have a hard, relatively smooth surface and are covered with fine pores, and, in contrast to true corals, do not have corallites or septa. Arising from the pores are numerous long hair-like tentacles, each bearing a number of tiny club-shaped mouthless stinging polyps specialised for food capture and defence. Between the stinging tentacles are smaller shorter tentacles which extend from larger pores; these are specialised for feeding and reproduction. Hydroid corals reproduce sexually by first producing jellyfish-like medusae which are released into the water. These free-living forms expel eggs and sperm. Fertilisation then takes place and the egg develops into a small larva which reproduces asexually to form the new polyp stage which settles on a reef and starts a new colony.

Hard Corals – Family Pocilloporidae

Club-horned corals Genus *Pocillopora*

The various species referred to as club-horned corals form rounded clumps of short, open branches with flattened club-like ends, the surface of which is covered by numerous wart-like projections. Corallites are small and sunken into the skeleton. Extended polyps give the colony a fuzzy appearance. Colonies range from 10-40 cm across and colours may be either green, brown or bluish grey. Occurs on both the tops and upper slopes of coral reefs.

Knob-horned corals Genus *Pocillopora*

Referred to as knob-horned corals, these species form dense bushy clusters with short stubby branches covered with numerous rounded projections. The polyps are often extended during the day, giving it a fuzzy appearance. The colours are usually pink, yellow or brown and colonies range from 10-30 cm across. This species is often found in exposed areas along rocky shores, but also extends down to 30 m on reefs along the East Coast. Occasionally found in tidal pools.

Smooth-horned corals Genus *Stylophora* (Unconfirmed)

The coral illustrated is thought to belong to the genus *Stylophora* but this requires confirmation. This common coral occurs on reefs in the Aliwal Shoal and Protea Banks areas, and ranges in depth from 15-40 m. The growth form is varied but typically forms flat, irregular-shaped branches with rounded tips extending horizontally from a common base or trunk. The surface of the coral appears smooth but is slightly rough to the touch. Colonies in shallower exposed areas are stunted, whereas those found in deeper protected areas have long slender branches forming colonies of up to 80 cm across. Usually brown or green in colour.

Hard Corals – Family Acroporidae

Prickly-pored corals Genus *Montipora*

Corals of this genus have growth forms ranging from leaf-like plates to undulating encrusting sheets. The corallites are small (2-3 mm) and poorly defined. The surface of the coral appears rough due to numerous small, irregular, wart-like projections. Colours are brown, green, pink or mauve. Colonies can attain a diameter of up to 2 m. Found on coral reefs and occasionally on rocky reefs as far south as the Aliwal Shoal area. Barnacles and fanworms often burrow into the skeletons of these corals.

Genus *Acropora*

Acropora is a diverse genus which comprises many species and is the dominant hard coral on most coral reefs. The growth form varies widely between species, but three kinds are particularly common: branching/staghorn, clusters, and plate-like formations. Individual species can also vary in growth form, depending on their exposure to water movement, light and sedimentation. The genus is characterised by a single axial corallite running through each branch, opening at the tip, and numerous small radial corallites, cylindrical in shape, surrounding the skeleton. Due to a light, porous skeleton, *Acropora* coral is relatively fast growing, compared to most other corals which have a denser skeleton.

Clustered finger corals Genus *Acropora*

These corals form closely spaced, short, uniform branches growing in a cluster from a basal plate. Colours are usually various shades of brown or pale green, and some species have purple tips. Colonies range from 20-40 cm across. This is a common species found in most coral reef habitats. Skeletons of this coral are often seen in souvenir shops.

Table corals Genus *Acropora*

Distinguished by their horizontally layered, open branches which radiate from a central or lateral stem, giving them a table-like appearance. The forked branches have numerous short, vertical branchlets. They are very brittle and are easily broken. Colonies may grow to 1 m across. Colours are brown, pale green or bluish grey. A common coral that occurs in most habitats on coral reefs.

Club-horned corals

Knob-horned corals

Smooth-horned corals

Prickly-pored corals

Clustered finger corals

Table corals

Staghorn corals Genus *Acropora*

Staghorn corals form irregular, loosely branched colonies which are usually pale green or cream in colour. The photograph shows just one of several species of staghorn coral. These fragile corals are confined to the more protected or deeper areas of coral reefs. Small fish often shelter in their branches. They are extremely vulnerable to damage by divers and fishermen.

Plate corals Genus *Acropora*

Plate corals develop solid flat plates which are attached to a central or lateral stem connected to the reef. They may have one or more plates of varying size and can grow to about 1,8 m across. Generally pale green or brown in colour. A common coral that occurs only on coral reefs, where it is found on both the tops and slopes of reefs down to depths of 40 m.

Hard Corals – Family Agariciidae

Contoured corals Genus *Pachyseris*

Pachyseris is a distinctive genus because the upper surface is covered with a series of concentric ridges and valleys. The corallites lie in the valleys and have very fine septa that cross the valleys at right angles. Growth forms can be leafy, encrusting, or plate-like, growing to 1 m or more across. Usual colours are brown, green or greyish blue. Occasionally colonies grow in a tiered formation on the side of a reef slope, creating an impressive sight. Confined to coral reefs where it prefers the deeper reef slopes and the edges of surge channels.

Hard Corals – Family Fungiidae

Mushroom corals Genus *Fungia*

Fungia is a distinctive genus that differs from other hard corals as it consists of a large, single, solitary polyp which is oval or elongate in shape. The mouth is housed in a central groove and is surrounded by numerous vertical partitions (septa) radiating from the centre, resembling an upturned mushroom. Juveniles are attached to the substratum by a short stalk, but soon break free; adults live loose on the bottom and are able to move around slowly, using their extended tentacles. The species illustrated grows to 15 cm in length and is usually brown or green in colour. Confined to coral reefs, it favours the deeper, more sheltered bottoms where it is often found amongst coral rubble. Regrettably, these corals have diminished in number in the Sodwana Bay marine reserve due to their illegal removal by divers.

Hard Corals – Family Portidae

Daisy corals (Diurnal corals) Genus *Goniopora*

Species of this genus form low, rounded colonies that grow to about 40 cm across. The polyps are closely spaced and have long stems that bear up to 24 daisy-like tentacles. They project as much as 20 mm above the skeleton, resembling a bunch of pale flowers. Colours are usually brown, grey or cream. This is the only hard coral that expands its polyps permanently during the day. It can easily be mistaken for a soft coral but when disturbed the polyps retract rapidly, revealing the skeleton below. The polyps are aggressive and will sting other corals to death. Occurs in most habitats on coral reefs down to a depth of 30 m.

Porous corals Genus *Porites*

Colonies of *Porites* species may be massive and boulder-like, growing to more than 3 m across, or flattish and encrusting, or branching or forming lobed clumps. The colony has closely spaced, very small (1-2 mm diameter), sunken corallites, often making the surface appear solid. Common colours are green, grey, brown and pink. The polyps hardly emerge from their corallites when feeding, but give the colony a fuzzy appearance. Large colonies are common and prominent on coral reefs but smaller ones can occur on rocky reefs and in sheltered tidal pools along the KwaZulu-Natal coast. Brightly coloured fanworms sometimes burrow into the skeleton of porous corals.

Staghorn corals

Plate corals

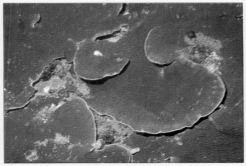

Contoured corals

Mushroom corals

Daisy corals

Porous corals

Hard Corals – Family Faviidae

False honeycomb corals Genus *Favia*

Species of this genus form domed or flattish colonies that can grow up to 80 cm across. They are covered with moderately large corallites (12 mm diameter) and are similar to the genus *Favites* (Honeycomb coral), except that the corallites have their own walls which are distinctly separated from the walls of adjacent corallites by a gap, or a continuous groove, if the walls are touching. Colours are extremely varied, with the centre of the corallites often being of a different colour than the edge. Found in most habitats on coral reefs down to 30 m. Isolated colonies also occur along the East Coast on shallow rocky reefs and in tidal pools.

Honeycomb corals Genus *Favites*

Colonies are flattish or dome-shaped, attaining 80 cm across. They are covered with moderately large corallites (12 mm diameter) and are similar to the genus *Favia* (False honeycomb coral), except that the corallites are joined together at their edges to form common walls with their neighbours, producing a honeycomb pattern. The colours are brown, bright green, grey or russet, with the centre of the corallites often being of a different colour than the edge. Found mainly on coral reefs down to 30 m, but occasionally occurs in tidal pools and on shallow reefs along the KwaZulu-Natal coast. There are many species in this genus, all difficult to tell apart.

Brain corals Genus *Oulophyllia*

Brain coral is the common name given to several coral genera with a brain-like appearance. Here it is used to describe the various species of the genus *Oulophyllia*. These corals form domed or flattish colonies up to 80 cm across. The corallites are fused together into short, discontinuous, meandering valleys which are much deeper and broader (10-12 mm valley width) than those of the similar genus *Platygyra* (Labyrinthine brain corals). The corallites have sharp ridges and finely toothed septa. The colour of the valleys is sometimes pale blue and that of the ridges either brown, green or grey. A common coral, found in most habitats on coral reefs down to a depth of 30 m.

Labyrinthine brain corals Genus *Platygyra*

Platygyra species form domed or flattish brain-like heads that may attain up to 1 m or more across. The corallites are fused together in rows to form long, sinuous valleys of about 5 mm wide between ridges. Very similar in appearance to the genus *Oulophyllia*, except that the ridges are more closely spaced. Live colonies present a striking network of green valleys and brown ridges, or green ridges on a khaki or white background. A common coral, generally confined to coral reefs where it occurs in most habitats down to a depth of 30 m.

Pimple corals Genus *Echinopora*

Echinopora species display various growth forms, from leaf-like plates to encrusting sheets that can attain 1 m or more across. Species of this coral are characterised by numerous large (8 mm diameter), irregularly spaced, pimple-like corallites which are separated by ridged or spiky areas. Usually green or brown, but occasionally dark blue or pinkish in colour. Generally confined to coral reefs, it occurs on both the tops and upper reef slopes down to depths of 40 m.

Hard Corals – Family Oculinidae

Spiky corals (Star corals) Genus *Galaxea*

Species of this genus form low rounded colonies averaging 30 cm across. The surface is distinctly spiky because the corallites project like turrets from the main skeleton and their septa are sharp and protruding. The polyps extend well beyond the septa and are nearly always extended during the daytime and have a star-like appearance. Colours are usually green or brown, and the tentacles usually have a distinct terminal white knob. Confined to coral reefs. The photograph shows both the living coral and the skeleton.

False honeycomb corals

Honeycomb corals

Brain corals

Labyrinthine brain corals

Pimple corals

Spiky corals

Hard Corals – Family Mussidae

False brain corals Genus *Lobophyllia*

Lobophyllia species have large, irregular-shaped corallites which average 3 cm across and are quite separate from one another. Although they appear fleshy, the corallites are prickly due to their large spiky septa. Colonies seldom exceed 30 cm across, and are usually green or brown and occasionally red or dark blue. Generally confined to coral reefs but occasionally seen as far south as Aliwal Shoal.

Hard Corals – Family Dendrophyliidae

Turbinate corals Genus *Turbinaria*

These impressive corals have funnel-like shapes, often with spirals, attached to the substratum by a trunk, or form encrusting sheets; colonies can attain 1,5 m or more across. The corallites only grow on the upper surface, and are relatively large (3-4 mm), protuberant and separated from one another by smooth areas. Polyps are sometimes extended during the day. Colours are usually pale green, yellowish brown or pale grey. Only occurs on coral reefs where it is found on the deeper reef slopes.

Green tree corals *Tubastrea micranthus*

This distinctive green tree coral species form large bushy, tree-like colonies which can grow to more than 1 m high. The corallites are separate, distinct and cylindrical in shape, protruding well above the coral surface. Colonies are covered with a layer of dark green or brownish-green fleshy tissue which usually appears deep black-green underwater, admired by divers for its beauty. A non-reef-building coral that lacks zooxanthellae; its colour is provided by its own pigments. The polyps are sometimes seen extended during the daytime. A deep-water coral, found on coral and rocky reefs along the East Coast and throughout the Indo-Pacific. Ranges in depth from 15-50 m and prefers areas of strong current. Provides refuge for small fish, such as the sea goldie (*Pseudanthias squamipinnis*).

Turret corals (Cup corals) *Dendrophyllia aurea*

Species referred to as turret corals form single tube-shaped corallites (10 mm wide) growing in small clusters from a common base. The large polyps resemble orange flowers, and are sometimes seen extended during the daytime. A non-reef-building coral that lacks zooxanthellae; its colour being provided by its own pigments. Abundant on East Coast reefs, it favours low light areas beneath overhangs and on shady rock faces.

Soft Corals – Family Alcyoniidae

Leather corals Genus *Lobophytum*

The genus *Lobophytum* includes many species with various growth forms. Typically forms low, creeping colonies with a smooth leathery surface having either low humps, folds, ridges or lobe projections. Surface is covered in retractable dimorphic polyps, large polyps (called autozooids, 0,5 mm diameter) and tiny polyps (siphonozooids) that lack tentacles and dot the surface. Some species are similar to the genus *Sinularia*, causing confusion. The species shown has a low, crumpled form, which may exceed 2 m across and is pale grey in colour. Other species are brown. A common soft coral found on the top and along slopes of coral reefs down to 30 m. Abundant on the Maputaland reefs.

Lobed soft corals Genus *Sinularia*

Species of this genus vary widely in growth form, but are usually low and flattish with an inconspicuous stalk, or erect with a thick, fleshy stalk. Their surface is rubbery and generally slimy to the touch, and may have crests, ridges, simple or branched lobes, or twisted walls. Colonies are often large and covered in identical short retractable polyps. Certain species are very similar in appearance to the genus *Lobophytum*. The species shown has clusters of small knobbly lobes at the end of a thick, fleshy stalk and can attain 1 m across. Colours are usually brown, pale yellow or greyish blue. Occasionally the polyps are seen extended during the day. Common on coral reefs, favouring the reef top and slopes, down to 30 m. Abundant on the Maputaland and southern Mozambique reefs.

False brain corals

Turbinate corals

Green tree corals

Turret corals

Leather corals

Lobed soft corals

Fleshy soft corals (Mushroom soft corals) Genus *Sarcophyton*

Forms roughly circular colonies with a characteristic convoluted, soft fleshy head attached to the substratum by a thick whitish stalk. It has dimorphic polyps, large stalked polyps (autozooids) and tiny polyps (siphonozooids) that lack tentacles and dot the surface. The polyps are often extended during daytime. When the polyps retract, the surface appears smooth. It can change its shape drastically by taking in water. The average colony diameter is 50 cm; the colour is either brown or pale yellow. Confined to coral reefs; common on Maputaland and southern Mozambique reefs.

Dead-man's fingers *Eleutherobia aurea*

Known as dead-man's fingers due to its shrivelled, finger-like appearance when contracted. This genus is characterised by its yellow lobe-shaped colonies with long white translucent retractable polyps. It is able to expand and contract with the aid of water. This species grows to about 15 cm in length and is abundant on reefs along southern and central KwaZulu-Natal, where it is found on the sides of rock faces and under ledges down to depths of 40 m. Easily mistaken for sponges when the polyps are retracted. Contracted and inflated colonies with extended polyps appear in the photograph.

Soft Corals – Family Nephtheidae

Thistle soft corals Genus *Dendronephthya*

This genus includes a variety of vividly coloured, tree-like soft coral species having almost translucent bodies, with polyps clustered in groups around branchlets extending from a thick, fleshy stem in which the sclerites are clearly visible when the colony is expanded. Often remains partially deflated during the day when not feeding. Inflates itself at night, enabling the colony to increase its surface area for feeding. Zooxanthellae is lacking in these corals, their bright colours being provided by pigments incorporated in their sclerites. The species shown has pink, yellow, mauve or red polyps with projecting white spikes (sclerites), giving it a prickly appearance. Occurs on the tops and edges of coral and rocky reefs, often in large numbers.

Branching soft corals Genus *Nephthea*

Very similar in appearance to *Dendronephthya*. Also forms tree-like colonies with almost translucent bodies. The polyps are clustered in groups around branchlets extending from a fleshy stem. The polyps of *Nephthea* lack spiky tips, giving the colony a less prickly appearance, more like a cauliflower. The small white polyps are often extended during daytime. Colours are usually cream, greyish, brownish to reddish. Lacks zooxanthellae; its colours being provided by pigments incorporated in its sclerites. Colonies are often solitary and occur on coral and rocky reefs at depths of 10-150 m.

Soft Corals – Family Xeniidae

Pulse corals Genus *Anthelia*

Colonies form small clusters of long-stalked polyps (15-40 mm) with feathery tentacles joined at the base to a membranous sheet attached to the substratum. These small, soft corals are conspicuous as their prominent feathery tentacles open and close rhythmically. The polyps are unable to fully retract like other soft corals. Colours vary, depending on species; cream, grey and brownish are common. Colonies are found on coral reefs at depths of 9-30 m.

Gorgonian Corals – Family Gorgoniidae

Palmate sea fans Genus *Leptogorgia*

Leptogorgia is a large genus with many gorgonian species. Colonies are profusely branched from a central stem, often in one plane; adjacent branches never fuse together to form bridges. Small white polyps adorn the branches and are able to withdraw into tiny rounded protuberances. The colour of species varies, but is usually white, yellow, orange or red. The species illustrated attains a height of 15 cm and has a distinctive red colour. Occurs on coral and rocky reefs along the East Coast at depths of 10-40 m. Often encountered in sandy depressions or gullies on deeper reefs.

Fleshy soft corals

Dead-man's fingers

Thistle soft corals

Branching soft corals

Pulse corals

Palmate sea fans

Gorgonian Corals – Family Melithaeidae

Acabaria sea fans Genus *Acabaria*

This relatively large genus has some 20 gorgonian species. Colonies are bushy and mostly branched in one plane. The branching is usually abundant with the tips of some adjacent branches fusing together to form bridges. The surface of the colony is dotted with knobs housing the polyps. Colours vary between species; red, orange, yellow or whitish are usual. The species shown attains a length of at least 40 cm and occurs on coral and rocky reefs along the East Coast at depths of 15-25 m. It is often encountered beneath overhangs and has a marked orientation to water movement.

Gorgonian Corals – Family Anthothelidae

Gorgonian twig corals *Homophyton verrucosum*

Endemic to southern Africa. Forms upright, single or sparsely branched colonies attaining 30 cm in height. The branches are covered with numerous small, hard, cylindrical protuberances (calyces), into which the polyps retract. Colours can be either red-orange with yellow protuberances or entirely yellow. Occurs at depths of 20-40 m on coral and rocky reefs, where it is found on the tops and bottoms of reef slopes. The photograph shows the tiny white polyps both extended and retracted.

Gorgonian Corals – Family Plexauridae

Bushy whip corals *Rumphella aggregata*

This gorgonian coral forms bushy colonies with long slender branches that are able to bend easily and resist strong water movement. The branches are covered by a thick cork-like layer (coenenchyme) containing zooxanthellae. The polyps are evenly distributed over the surface of the branches and appear as dark dots when retracted. The polyps are sometimes seen extended during the day, giving the branches a furry appearance. The colour of the colonies is usually dull; commonly greyish, brownish, or pale bluish to lavender-grey. Colonies may attain a height of up to 1 m. Commonly encountered on sandy depressions or gullies on coral reefs at depths of 15-20 m.

Black Corals – Family Antipathidae

Whip corals (Wire corals) Genus *Cirrhipathes*

The various species in this genus form long, unbranched colonies extending from a base attached to the reef. Colonies may grow to 3 m or more in length and can be straight, bent or coiled. Colours vary from pale green, yellow, brown or grey. The polyps cannot be fully retracted, which gives the colony a barbed-wire-like appearance. Whip coral is found in deep water, usually below 15 m, and occurs on coral and rocky reefs throughout the Indo-Pacific.

Branched black corals Genus *Antipathes*

Plant- and tree-like forms typify the species of this genus. The silvery-coloured species shown here has feathery branches resembling a frost-covered tree, and is much admired by divers for its stunning beauty. Colonies may grow to 1,5 m in size and are found in deep water below 18 m on coral and rocky reefs ranging from the Eastern Cape northwards; particularly common in the Aliwal Shoal area. Small fish often seek refuge in the branches of these corals.

Hydroid Corals – Family Milleporidae

Fire corals (Stinging corals) Genus *Millepora*

Recognised by its smooth surface and form. *Millepora* comprises several species with a variety of growth forms; branching, encrusting growths, and colonies with irregular vertical plates. Like other hydrozoans, it can give a nettle-like sting. Colour is brownish yellow with pale yellow or whitish tips. Size of colonies varies but can reach several metres across. Generally confined to coral reefs where it is relatively common on reef tops and shallow reef slopes. Uncommon on the Maputaland reefs.

Acabaria sea fans

Gorgonian twig corals

Bushy whip corals

Whip corals

Branched black corals

Fire corals

GLOSSARY

Abdomen - belly

Aggregation - group of fish, not all swimming in the same direction, i.e. as opposed to a shoal

Algae - a low form of aquatic plant-life

Anal fin - a fin just below the tail

Anterior - the front or head of the fish

Ascidian - a sessile marine animal with a sac-like body, eg. sea-squirt or redbait

Axis - main stem or cylinder

Barbel - a fleshy projection near the mouth, used for taste, smell or touch

Bony fishes - fishes with a true bone skeleton

Brackish - water that is neither totally fresh, nor as salty as pure seawater

Calcareous - composed of calcium carbonate or chalk

Carnivorous - feeding on animals

Cartilaginous - composed of gristle; descriptive of fishes which lack true bony skeletons, eg. sharks, skates and rays

Caudal fin - the unpaired fin at the tail

Caudal peduncle - narrow region attaching the caudal fin to the body

Coenenchyme - the tissue connecting adjoining polyps in a colony of cnidarians

Colony - a group of polyps that are interconnected and genetically identical

Compressed - flattened shape of body from side to side

Corallite - the part of a coral skeleton housing an individual polyp

Crustaceans - a large group of mostly aquatic invertebrate animals, e.g. prawns, crabs, crayfish

Deep-bodied - shape of fish where the height is greater in relation to the length

Depressed - flattened from top to bottom

Disc - fused head and fin region of some depressed fish

Disc width - the 'wingspan' of rays

Dimorphic - colonies that have two different types of polyps

Dorsal - pertaining to the back and upper region of the fish

East Coast - the coastline including the Eastern Cape from East London northwards to Mozambique

Eelgrass - a flowering marine plant that occurs in bays and estuaries

Elongated - shape of fish where the length is greater in relation to the height

Embryo - a developing organism prior to hatching or birth

Endemic - limited to a particular geographic region

Estuary - the widening channel of a river where it nears the sea, and where salinities fluctuate

Filamentous - thread-like, eg. fins and algae

Fins - organs of propulsion and balance

Family - a major entity in the classification of animals and plants which consists of related genera

Genus - a group of closely related animal or plant species with similar characteristics

Gill - respiratory organ

Gill cover - bony plate protecting the gills of bony fish

Gill opening - opening behind the head, protected by the gill cover through which exhaled water is passed

Gill raker - projection on the gill arches that filters food from water

Gorgonin - a tough fibrous hornlike protein which is dark brown or black in colour, and forms the internal axis of some gorgonians

Habitat - environment of an organism

Hydrozoa - small animal related to and resembling sea anemones

Indo-Pacific - embracing the Indian and western Pacific Ocean

Intertidal zone - shoreline between high and low water

Invertebrate - animal without a backbone

Lateral line - the line that runs lengthwise

Median fins - the fins in the median plane, hence the dorsal, anal and caudal fins

Mesenteries - radial partitions within the gastrovascular cavity of the coral polyp

Midwater - area between the surface of the water and sea-bed

Mollusc - an invertebrate, usually with an outer shell

Mucus - slimy fluid produced by the skin

Octocoral - member of the phylum Coelenterata, characterised by eight feathery tentacles surrounding the mouth of each polyp

Omnivorous - feeding on plant and animal

Pectoral - chest or breast region

Pelagic - living in the open sea

Pelvic - related to the pelvis or hind limbs posterior to the belly

Pharyngeal teeth - teeth located in the throat behind the gills

Plankton - tiny animals (zooplankton) or plants (phythoplankton) which float or drift in the water

Polyp - cylindrical animal, attached at one end, bearing a mouth and tentacles

Posterior - the rear of fish

Ray - a cartilaginous and jointed fin support

Sclerite - a particle of calcium carbonate found in most octocorals

Septa - vertical plate-like structures that radiate from the wall towards the centre of the corallite, alternating with mesenteries

Sessile - attached or stationary

Shoal - group of fish swimming in the same direction

Spine - a sharp, unjointed projection, often a part of the fin

Species - the fundamental unit in the classification of animals and plants consisting of a population of individuals which freely interbreed with one another

Substratum - a rock or solid object to which an animal or plant can attach itself

Subtidal - below the lowest level on the shore reached by the tides

Symbiosis - a relationship between different animals where both parties benefit

Tunicates - a group of minute, primitive, sedentary marine animals having a sac-like, unsegmented body

Ventral - pertaining to the lower region or underside of fish

Water column - the body of water between the sea-bed and surface

Zooplankton - the animal component of plankton suspended in the water column

Zooxanthellae - microscopic single-celled algae that are symbiotic in the bodies of some animals

---

SUGGESTED FURTHER READING

Allen, G. & Steene, R. 1987. *Reef Fishes of the Indian Ocean.* T.F.H. Publications Inc. USA.

Branch, G. & M. 1981. *The Living Shores of Southern Africa.* C. Struik, Cape Town.

Branch, M. 1987. *Explore the Seashore of South Africa.* Struik Publishers, Cape Town.

Branch, G. & M., Griffiths, C. & Beckley, L. 1994. *Two Oceans - A Guide to the Marine Life of Southern Africa.* David Philip Publishers, Cape Town.

Burgess, W., Axelrod, H. & Hunziker, R. 1988. *Dr Burgess's Atlas of Marine Aquarium Fishes.* T.F.H. Publications Inc. USA.

Compagno, L., Ebert, D. & Smale, M. 1989. *Guide to the Sharks and Rays of Southern Africa.* Struik Publishers, Cape Town.

Dakin, N. 1992. *The Book of the Marine Aquarium.* Salamander Books LTD, UK.

Griffiths, C. & R. 1988. *Struik Pocket Guide Series: Seashore Life of Southern Africa.* Struik Publishers, Cape Town.

Lieske, E. & Myers, R. 1994. *Collins Pocket Guide: Coral Reef Fishes.* Harper Collins Publishers, Johannesburg.

Smith, M. & Heemstra, P., (eds.) 1988. *Smith's Sea Fishes.* Southern Book Publishers, Johannesburg.

Van Der Elst, R. 1986. *Struik Pocket Guide Series: Sharks and Stingrays.* Struik Publishers, Cape Town.

Van Der Elst, R. 1988. *A Guide to the Common Sea Fishes of Southern Africa.* Struik Publishers, Cape Town.

Van Der Elst, R. 1990. *Everyone's Guide to Sea Fishes of Southern Africa.* Struik Publishers, Cape Town.

Williams, G. 1993. *Coral Reef Octocorals.* Natural Science Museum, Durban.

Wood, E. 1983. *Corals of the World.* T.F.H. Publications, USA.

INDEX TO SCIENTIFIC NAMES

Corals

Fishes

INDEX TO AFRIKAANS NAMES *(English common names in parentheses)*

Fishes

INDEX TO COMMON NAMES